SCIENCE AND CHRIST

PIERRE TEILHARD DE CHARDIN

SCIENCE AND CHRIST

TRANSLATED
FROM THE FRENCH BY
RENÉ HAGUE

HARPER & ROW, PUBLISHERS

New York and Evanston

SCIENCE ET CHRIST
was first published in France
by Éditions du Seuil in 1965

CONTENTS

This book consists of papers more directly
concerned with religious problems, written
by Pierre Teilhard de Chardin
during the years 1919–1955 and here presented
in chronological order.

EDITORIAL NOTE

As in previous volumes, we should draw attention to the fact that the papers printed here were never revised by the author with a view to publication. They are, accordingly, offered to the reader simply as working material.

What Père Teilhard says at the head of *Christianity and Evolution*[1] applies in varying degrees to all the other essays: 'I am writing this simply as a personal contribution to the common task shared by all Christian minds, expressing what, in my own particular case, is demanded by the *fides quaerens intellectum*. I am not putting forward a definite statement or teaching, but offering suggestions.' Thus, 'anything in my thought that may be fruitful—or, on the contrary, open to criticism—will emerge more clearly. What is living in it will have a chance of surviving and growing. And then my work will have been done.'

[1] To be included in a later volume.

For my own part, I am convinced that there is no more substantial natural nourishment for the religious life than contact with properly understood scientific realities. (. . .) No one can understand so well as the man who is absorbed in the study of matter, to what a degree Christ, through his Incarnation, is internal to the world, how much he is rooted in the world even in the very heart of the tiniest atom.

('*Science and Christ*', *27 February 1921.*)

I am struck by the fact that the Church almost entirely lacks an *organ of research* (in contrast with everything that lives and progresses around her). Yet she will never keep the faith luminous for her children and for those outside her except by *seeking*, in a quest for what is felt to be a matter of life or death. (. . .)

There must, then, be organised and developed, under the direction of the Ecclesia *docens*, the Ecclesia *quaerens*.

(*Letter to Père Fontoynont, 26 July 1917.*)

SCIENCE AND CHRIST

CHAPTER I

WHAT EXACTLY IS THE HUMAN BODY?

---

a. Even a single attempt to determine exactly what the body of a living being consists in, is sufficient to make one realise that 'my body'—an entity that is so clear when we remain in the practical sphere—is, when we come to theory, extremely difficult to define and pin down.

We may decide to restrict the body to those elements that live strictly *with the life of the living being*: and in that case we find that it is reduced to a mere tangle of nervous fibres.

Or we may try to extend it to everything that is subject to the dominating and organising activity of the soul: and in that case we have to include in it elements that are manifestly *without life* in the normal sense of the word (such as the inanimate cells of bone and blood), or possess a life that is completely autonomous (amoebae)—and of these it is well-nigh impossible to hold that they are the *personal, incommunicable,* property of the living being.

b. We meet the difficulty in a new and more lively form when we pass from just a body in general, to the body of Christ. What, in Christ, is the matter which undergoes the hypostatic union, what is the *matter that claims our worship*?

Are we to worship the drops of blood that fell from our Master on the blackthorn in the hedgerow?

And the almost independently existing cells that were to be found throughout the flesh of Christ on earth (as in all human flesh)—did they, *in their own amoeba-life,* enjoy the honour of being hypostatically united to the Word—an honour that was not granted even to the Blessed Virgin Mary?

c. All these improbabilities and strange questions make it perfectly clear that the normal idea of the 'human body' is not patient of philosophical criticism. We may try to ease them or get around them one by one, but we are simply wasting our time. The subtle distinctions and individual explanations we pile up in an attempt to retain in philosophy the empirical notion of 'Body' are simply patches sewn into a worn-out fabric. The very basis of our speculations about matter is defective. We must understand bodies in some other way than that we have hitherto accepted. The problem is how.

Perhaps this may be the way:
d. Hitherto, the prevailing view has been that the body (that is to say, the matter that is *incommunicably* attached to each soul) is a *fragment* of the universe—a piece *completely detached* from the rest and handed over to a spirit that informs it.

e. In future, we shall say that the Body is the very Universality of things, in as much as they are centred on an animating Spirit, in as much as they influence that Spirit—and are themselves influenced and sustained by it. For a soul, to have a body is to be ἐγκεκοσμισμένη.[1]

f. The action of the individual, it is true, radiates from an organic centre that is more specially mobile—from a group of lower monads that form a more effective 'colony'. But the *sphere of immanent operation* extends in reality to something that belongs to the whole universe.

[1] *Enkekosmismenē*: rooted in the cosmos. (Ed.)

g. My own body is not these cells or those cells that *belong exclusively* to me: it is *what*, in these cells *and* in the rest of the world feels my influence and reacts against me. *My* matter is not a *part* of the universe that I possess *totaliter*: it is the *totality* of the Universe possessed by me *partialiter*.

h. Thus, the limited, tangible fragments that in common usage we call monads, molecules, bodies, are *not complete* beings. They are only the nucleus of such beings, their organisational centre. In each case, the real extension of these bodies coincides with the full dimensions of the universe.

i. From this point of view, we see that the world is no longer like an aggregate of inter-fused elements, but a single sphere with countless centres from which it can be observed and from which action can emanate. It is multiple, *not as a heap of stones* is (a sum of juxtaposed parts), but as a *gaseous mixture* is (in which each gas fills the whole volume of the mixture)— though that is a lamentably crude comparison.

Since each element is strictly co-extensive with all the others, with the whole, it is really a microcosm.

Universal World=World centred on Peter+World centred on Paul, and so on.[2]

[2] Undated. Père Teilhard may have been referring to this note in the letter he wrote to Marguerite Teillard-Chambon on 5 September 1919: 'Finally, I've recently written eight pages on the way in which one should understand the limits of the human body. I mention this, because Valensin told me he was delighted with what I wrote and wants to send it to Blondel.' (*The Making of a Mind*, p. 306). But the very shortness of the text—perhaps a summary or a first draft—itself presents a difficulty.

CHAPTER II

NOTE ON THE UNIVERSAL CHRIST

By the Universal Christ, I mean Christ the organic centre of the entire universe.

Organic centre: that is to say the centre on which every even natural development is ultimately physically dependent.

Of the entire universe: that is to say, the centre not only of the earth and mankind, but of Sirius and Andromeda, of the angels, of all the realities on which we are physically dependent, whether in a close or a distant relationship (and that, in all probability, means the centre of all participated being).

Of the entire universe, again, that is to say, the centre not only of moral and religious effort, but also of all that that effort implies—in other words of all physical and spiritual growth.

This Universal Christ is the Christ presented to us in the Gospels, and more particularly by St Paul and St John. It is the Christ by whom the great mystics lived: but nevertheless not the Christ with whom theology has been most concerned.

The purpose of this note is to bring to the notice of my friends, more skilled than I am in sacred science and better placed to exert intellectual influence, how necessary, how vitally necessary, it now is that we should make plain this eminently Catholic notion of Christ α and ω.[1]

---

[1] Alpha and Omega. (Ed.)

a. In the first place, as I have explained elsewhere, the present history of religious sentiment in men, *whoever they may be,* seems to me to be dominated by a sort of revelation, emerging in human consciousness, of the one great universe.

Faced by the physical immensity that is thus revealed to our generation, some (the unbelievers) turn away from Christ *a priori,* because an image of him is often presented to them that is manifestly more insignificant than the world. Others, better informed (and this includes many believers), nevertheless feel that a fight to the death is going on within them. *Which will be the greater* they will have to face, and which, therefore, will command their worship—Christ or the universe? The latter is continually growing greater, beyond all measure. It is absolutely essential that the former should be officially, and explicitly, set above all measure.

If the unbelievers are to begin to believe, and the believers to continue to do so, we must hold up before men the figure of the Universal Christ.

b. To some this need for the Universal Christ may appear unwarranted, artificial, subjective. For their part, they have no such feeling.

To these I should not hesitate to answer, 'Well, I can only be sorry for you.'

But I can add this: Quite apart from any subjective desire, *even you* are bound to accept the Universal Christ. He is in fact the only reality that can now give balance to dogma *in se.* We have (since the earliest times, and fortunately) lavishly accorded to Christ the attributes of universal mediation: 'Omnia in ipso, per ipsum . . .'. Has it been noted that, as the universe is seen to be more immense in its determinisms, its past, and its extension, so those attributes become an uncommonly heavy burden for our classical philosophy and theology? Under the constant flood of being that science lets loose, a certain

15

small-scale academic Christ is swept away; and instead the great Christ of tradition and mysticism is revealed and must be accepted: and it is to this Christ that we must turn.

c. In studying the Universal Christ we do more than offer the world, whether believing or unbelieving, a more attractive figure. We impose upon theology (dogmatic, mystical, moral) a complete recasting: and this will be effected *automatically*, vitally, smoothly, *exercite*[2] simply by the fact that Christian thought will be at pains to bring out the features of the Universal Christ; it will be the Christ whom it has always worshipped though without understanding explicitly enough how immense is the value of that attribute of universality. We must say, then:

1. *If Christ is to be truly universal*, the Redemption, and hence the Fall, must extend to the whole universe. Original sin accordingly takes on a *cosmic nature* that tradition has always accorded to it, but which, in view of the new dimensions we recognise in our universe, obliges us radically to restate the historical representation of that sin and the too purely juridical way in which we commonly describe its being passed on.

2. If it is to be possible for the universe to have been affected as one whole by an accident that occurred in certain souls, then its coherence '*in unitate materiae et in unitate spiritus*' must be infinitely greater than we used generally to admit. *To conform to the evidence of dogma*, the world can no longer be an agglomeration of juxtaposed objects: we must recognise it as one great whole, welded together and evolving organically. The theoreticians of Christianity will have to overhaul the whole metaphysics of the One and the Multiple, if we wish our philosophy to meet the demands of our theology.

3. If Christ is universal (if, in other words, he is gradually consummated from all created being) it follows that his king-

---

[2] *Exercite*: unremittingly. (Ed.)

dom, in its essence, goes beyond the domain of the life that is, in a strict sense, called supernatural. Human action can be related to Christ, and can co-operate in the fulfilment of Christ, not only by the intention, the fidelity, and the obedience in which—as an addition—it is clothed, but also by the actual *material content* of the work done. All progress, whether in organic life or in scientific knowledge, in aesthetic faculties or in social consciousness, can therefore be made Christian even in its object (since all progress, *in se*, is organically integral with spirit, and spirit depends on Christ). To realise this very simple fact is to tear down the distressing barrier that, *in spite of everything, still stands*, in our present theorising, between Christian and human effort. Human effort becomes divinisable *in opere*[3] (and not only *in operatione*), and so for the Christian the world becomes divine in its entirety. The whole of our ascetical and mystical doctrine is thereby given a new vitality.

4. If this work, finally, of Christ's fulfilment is to have a meaning, is to be worth what it has cost God, the mysterious *Compound* formed by Christ and the universe (by the universe centred on Christ) must have a specific and unique value. The worship of the Universal Christ will direct Christian thought to the extremely important, though often too lightly dismissed, question of the value of souls *in se*: in other words, of the value of the world, or, in short, of the reason for the Creation. At a time when human thought is coming to recognise the cosmos as a whole *per se*, it would be as well to devote some thought to the relationship that unites that whole to God. We need not look far for an answer: creation by love, outward glory. But is this all that is contained in the deposit of revelation?

[3] The value of my act is measured not only by the purity of my intention but also by the objective rightness of its term. 'He who does what is true comes to the light' (John 3. 21). This, it will be noted, is one of the principal themes of *Le Milieu Divin*, Eng. trans., Collins, London, and Harper & Row, New York (*The Divine Milieu*), 1960, Fontana, 1964. (Ed.)

To investigate the question of the Universal Christ is ultimately, we now see, to direct our thoughts, our prayer, to relate progress, to the natural centre of all Christian thought, to the very quick of the life of the Church today.

If, when this has been understood, we compare the way in which tradition has developed in relation first to the κεχαριτωμένη[4] of the angelic salutation, and secondly to the theory of the Universal Christ as expounded in whole chapters of St Paul, we will be amazed: on the one hand, we see a branch, emerging from a small lateral bud, bursting into full bloom; on the other, the actual leading shoot of the Christian tree, swollen with sap, and at the same time practically unchanged since the first century of the Church.

If we look for an explanation of this radical difference, I shall answer that it is to be found, in the first place, in the very way in which human thought develops. In order passionately to love Our Lady, all that used to be required of Christians was to become more completely refined, sensitive, human. That stage came in with the middle ages. Passionately to love the great universe, and to feel the imperative need to clothe Christ in it, required from men a prolonged effort of observation, thought and self-possession. This means being seriously concerned with matters of a new order, and even today we are only just beginning to be explicitly aware of their urgency.

There is, I believe, another reason, less profound but more immediate, for the stagnation, since the time of St Paul, of the concept of the Universal Christ. This is the excessive emphasis in philosophy on logical, moral and juridical relationships. It is simpler, safer (*tutius*), more convenient (as Our Lord's example shows), to express the relations between God and man as family or domestic relationships. Such analogies are true, in as much as union in Christ is effected between persons,

---

[4] *Kekharitōmenē*: full of grace. (Ed.)

but they are incomplete. If we are to express the whole truth we must correct them by analogies drawn from realities that are specifically *natural* and *physical*. The friendship of God and adoption by God are expressions that include an adaptation of the universe, a transformation, a recasting, that are organic and cannot be cancelled. Any expression of God's free will is a particular modification of all the determinisms of the cosmos. So long as we remain in the simple domain of juridical and moral relationships, the immature philosophy of certain theologians has little difficulty in explaining the Kingship of Christ.[5] But when we adopt the 'organic' point of view, the central dignity of Christ is seen to be a vast all-embracing Reality—that remodels and recasts every belief, every observance and every system, adapting them to its own service.

It is, I imagine, because their thinking has not been sufficiently governed by this principle of *the primacy of the organic over the juridical* that theologians have for so long been able to remain insensitive to the fundamental mystery of the Universal Christ.

Today, 'popular' human and Christian consciousness has the duty of reminding the masters of Israel that the time will never come when we are entitled to fold our arms and rest content with any doctrine, however convenient it may be. 'What we are seeking is something that is One, that is organic, because it is thus that Christ is seen by us in the depths of our hearts.' In these latter days, this is what many souls are saying.

Is not this because the time has come for the still dormant stem of the tree to resume its growth? It is, surely, no exaggeration to say that a new cycle is opening for the Church,

---

[5] Because it can be explained simply by regarding it as an extrinsic conveyance of the world to Christ—a notion similar to what we call 'right of ownership', for example.

wonderfully adapted to the present age of mankind: the cycle of Christ worshipped through the universe.

Those who believe they can hear the coming of the Master, should keep watch, should kindle their desires, should work.

Paris, January 1920

CHAPTER III

SCIENCE AND CHRIST
OR ANALYSIS AND SYNTHESIS

*Remarks on the way in which the scientific study of
matter can and must help to lead us up to the divine centre*

My friends,

For men who are destined, as you are, to combine scientific
work and Christian effort in one and the same life, it is essential that the mutual relationship of the two spheres of 'Science
and Religion' should be defined with the utmost possible
clarity. It is all the more necessary to see them accurately in
that the attempts of apologetics in this connexion have not
always been very well balanced. Sometimes apologists have
stood out against indisputable discoveries; sometimes they
have tried to deduce from scientific facts philosophical or theological conclusions that the study of phenomena is incapable
of providing. Sometimes science is presented as an evil force,
as a tempter, as black magic; sometimes it is extolled as
a divine illumination, as a truly novel task offered to the
Christian's ambition.

I do not propose today to deal directly with the question of
discovering what it is that makes science valuable, and even
indispensable, for the full development of the Christian; all I
shall try to do, as an introduction to that fundamental question, is *to make you love science in a Christian way*, by establishing
the two following propositions:

1. Because the scientific study of the world is analytical, at
first it makes us follow a direction that leads away from divine
realities.

21

2. On the other hand, since this same scientific insight into things shows us the *synthetic structure* of the world, it obliges us to reverse our direction and, by its natural extension, turns us back to the unique centre of things, which is God our Lord.

1. The inability of science to find God in the course of its analytical procedures

Whatever the extreme pragmatists, the utilitarians, may say, what man seeks throughout his life, what he strives for more than for his daily bread and any material well-being, is knowledge. The very essence of our life is our urge not for a better life, but for a fuller degree of life. And an instinct stronger than the remonstrances of sceptics and false prophets warns us that if we are to have a fuller degree of life we must first have more knowledge.

Deeply rooted in the minds of all of us is the conviction that a mysterious fire lies hidden somewhere around us, and that if we are to be happy we must get possession of it as a torch to shed light on our understanding of the profound significance of the world, as the instrument with which we may master and remodel things. Mankind has always, as it still does, lived by this obstinate hope that by investigating nature we shall be able to discover the secret of the real, put our hand on the underlying forces that control the growth of beings: that we may read the secret, track down the source. And scientific research, for all its claim to be positivist, is coloured and haloed—or rather is irresistibly animated, when you get to the bottom of it, by a mystical hope.

Thus the essential urge of our mind is to try to penetrate to the heart of the world. In what direction, however, should we turn our steps if we are to arrive at the point we are seeking, where every obscurity will be dissipated in light and every antagonism become the obedient servant of our action?

For some time, no doubt, men were able to imagine that the secret of the world was hidden in the remote distances of geography. If, they thought, we could make our way to the most distant or inaccessible parts of the earth, if we could climb the peaks of Olympus, penetrate the depths of the forests, track down the source of the great rivers, set foot in the antipodes, descend into the bowels of the impenetrable earth, then we should certainly find the dwelling place of souls or of the Gods. We should reach a further extension, or even another side, of things. A great voyage, a resolute feat of endurance, was all that was required to bring us face to face with the mystery that puzzles us. The only veil between us and the divine was the opacity of bodies or the mists on the horizon.

Long before methodical exploration had girdled the earth and sounded its depths, we smiled, my friends, at these childish dreams. We had only to think a little to realise that we would never find anything but what was like ourselves in a survey of the universe confined to its surface. The world is made up of successive zones, escalated planes of concentric spheres of existence, giving access one to another. To know more, we must leave the circle upon which life as it is now moves. The light will emerge only when we go deeper. We shall see its radiance only if we leave behind the outer husk of beings and succeed in discovering what is hidden deep down in them. When man had understood that he could journey round all things without finding anything that would enable him to understand them, he decided to penetrate into them.

But what exactly do we mean by the metaphor of 'penetrating into the depths of things'? Every being has two poles, a lower pole from which it emerges, and a higher pole towards which it ascends. In which direction can it be penetrated and explained? In the exactly determined direction that leads down into the secret of bodies, or along the shadowy road that climbs up to the extensions of the soul?

For the great majority of men, the question does not even seem to arise. If we want to know what is inside a house, we open the door—in a watch, we strip it down—in a walnut, we crack it. The first step taken by the mind that wants to know what something is made of, is to take it to pieces and analyse it. The whole of science is derived from this instinctive act. Science is essentially an analysis. Its method of enquiry and its conclusions are governed by the principle that the secret of things lies in their elements, so that in order to understand the world all we have to do is to arrive at the most simple of the terms from which it has emerged.

You know as well as I do the astonishing progress achieved by twentieth-century man in his work of analysing the real.

1. In the sphere of inanimate matter, we have effected an astonishing visual segregation of its higher and lower elements. Extremely accurate measurements have enabled us to plot the positions of the stars in space and to determine their speed; photographic methods and enlargements have picked out the individual elements of the nebulae and brought to light thousands of new stars in the vault of heaven; thus, at a level above ourselves, we are beginning to form an idea of the sidereal structure of the universe. And we are overwhelmed as we discover that the higher 'macroscopic' unit of the world, its largest known molecule, is the spiral nebula: millions of galaxies gravitating in space until they are lost in its infinite remoteness.

Turning our analysis, then, to the domain of the microscopic, we have seen Pascal's second infinite revealed to our eyes. First visually, and then indirectly by methods of remarkable ingenuity and accuracy, we have disclosed within matter an astonishing series of natural units that decrease in size: colloidal particles that dance under the ultra-microscope, molecules that travel in electrolytes or are in constant motion in gases, fragments of electric atoms that we can now count and weigh, and follow through the minute phases of their gravitation.

2. Just as science has, optically or chemically, broken down inorganic matter, so it has effected a parallel disintegration in the domain of organic matter. In turn, the living has been found to be composed of cells—and the cells of protoplasm and nucleus. It was thought that the breaking down was complete. Far from it. The nucleus is now known to be extremely complex, and its almost incredibly complicated nuclear structure is itself built up on a 'Protean' fabric that has not yet been fully analysed but has been accurately pinned down. Thus in our very flesh and bones we find not only a cellular but a chemical multiplicity: and this coincidence allows us to include living substance in the progressively decreasing series of molecules and electrons.

3. While science was breaking down the material elements of the world, it was at the same time dismantling their sources of energy. The extreme complexity of physico-chemical processes, from those that cause the awe-inspiring gravitation of the stars to those that cause the vibration of the most recent particles to be discovered by our research, has gradually been reduced to a group of relatively simple components. The whole balance of the world can be contained in a group of equations that govern two energies (electro-magnetic and gravitational)[1] and, subject to certain conditions, are expressible in a group of equations with four variables. Each reinforcing the other, the analysis of masses and that of energies have effected so advanced a breaking down of things into their natural elements, that all we are coming to see as the ultimate texture of the world is an incredible plurality of inordinately

_____

[1] Had Teilhard been writing this passage today, he would have added the reactions discovered since 1921: what are known as low-level reactions (Beta radioactivity) and nuclear reaction. (Ed.)

simplified particles; of these it is impossible to say what distinguishes them one from another, or what marks them off from the medium in which they float. These ultimate particles are so numerous and so little individualised that they seem to form a continuous layer of energy.

4. So: the active, experimental, analysis conducted by science has introduced us to this infinitely dissociated world; and now a different method is at hand to assure us that this is not a fictitious reality, an artificial product of our action upon the real. If we follow the *spatial* study of bodies considered in the present by a study of them *in time*, if we observe their history, we shall find that they dissolve and disintegrate in accordance with the same law. No organic (or inorganic) being does in fact appear in a completely finished state or fully formed. It presents itself to our experience as resting upon an endless series of earlier states (different states of condensation of matter, forms of life that have gradually been roughed out). If we try to trace back this chain of successive states to their source, this is what we shall find: at the end of a descent into the past that can be compared only to the descent into minuteness achieved by chemical analysis of material masses, we come back to the world of particles. Historical analysis of the past joins hands with physico-chemical analysis of the present. Whether we make our way back scientifically to the temporal origins of the world, or whether we penetrate into the secrets of its present structure, in either case everything is equally reduced to a swarming of elements governed exclusively by the statistical laws of large numbers and of chance.

Thus, my friends, we see that scientific analysis has succeeded in its attempts even beyond its hopes. We wanted to crack the shell and open things up: things *yielded* with surprising ease. As we hammered away, break followed break, and things were gradually reduced to something of which it is impossible

26

to say whether it is matter or force. Everything has dissolved into a sort of energy possessing the rudiments of mass and structure, which represents both the most general form of the world's present substances and the initial reservoir from which its whole past appears to emerge.

At the end of this great and highly successful effort, have we come closer to the central point at which we were aiming? Are we nearer the heart of things, nearer their secret, their source? Can we at last put our hands on the explanation?

We can: but not in the way it has often been understood.

The first thing a man thinks when scientific analysis has led him *to the extreme lower limits* of matter is that in these ultimate particles of matter he really holds the very essence of the riches of the universe. '*The elements contain in themselves the virtue of the whole: to hold the elements is to possess the whole.*' That is the principle implicitly accepted by a number of scientists and even philosophers. Were that principle true, we should have to say that science forces us back into materialism. As scientific analysis has progressed, in fact, so everything that is 'soul' has gradually appeared to vanish from our outlook; the creative and providential power that directs the world has gradually degenerated, in the eyes of science, into a cluster of evolutionary laws—freedom into determinisms—organic life into physico-chemical phenomena—light into vibrations—molecules into electrons. One after the other, Godhead, morality, life, feeling, continuity . . . have been wiped out, to be replaced by a swarm of ever more impersonal elements. If analysis has in truth brought us to the centre of things, that is, *to the extreme point of their reality and their consistence*, then goodbye to spirit—goodbye to the reign of spirit, to its primacy! Everything is, ultimately, nothing but plurality and unconsciousness.

Let us see if we can find an answer to that.

If, my friends, we are to break the deadly spell of materialism and so rediscover the spiritual world without repudiating science, all we have to do is to tell ourselves this: 'Analysis is necessary, and is good: but it has not brought us where we thought it would.' Materialism is born from a fundamental error of perspective. We often think that science has introduced us to the essential spheres of the world, to the most concentrated areas of the universe, to the domain of the consistent and the absolute. In fact, by following science, we have gone no further than *the extreme lower limits of the real*, where beings are at their most impoverished and tenuous. We were looking for unity, for synthesis: we have found them both, but we have not found the higher synthesis of richness, nor the unity that comes from concentration—what we have attained is the unity of impoverishment in the homogeneous, the synthesis that comes from the attenuation of specific characteristics.[2]

Consider for a moment what, when finally weighed up, science has left us with which to reconstruct the world—atoms more or less dissolved in a formless energy. Not much, indeed, and that far down the scale of reality. But can we say that it is at any rate something, that it has some solidity, some stability, something in it of the immortal and absolute? Indeed, we cannot. If we look more closely at the ultimate material residuum at which analysis has come to a halt in our time, we shall recognise that it represents no more than a sort of low-level nebula. It is something unresolved. It may be that we shall never succeed in breaking down the real further than the point we have now reached. We should not conclude, however, that we have touched the rock-bottom of resistance, a prime element of things, an unresolvable simplicity, an eternal substratum. The whole of our scientific experience tells us that this is not so: below the electron, below energy, matter

2 What is called scientific 'synthesis' (cf. the general theory of the transmission of gravity) is simply the reduction of the real *to a smallest common element*.

can still be analysed, it can still be broken down indefinitely into natural elements, both in time and space. There are no such things as atoms in the etymological sense of the word. Matter is essentially boundless plurality, mere dust. It is therefore impossible to build upon it, and to try to follow it up to its very end would be to move towards nothingness. Matter is not a stable foundation of the world: it is a direction in which things continually disappear a little more as they lose a little more unity.

We had to get down to 'atoms' in order to realise this truth, but now we must never forget it: in our analysis we have allowed what constitutes the value and the solidity of beings to escape from us. The *only consistence* beings have comes to them from their *synthetic element*, in other words from what, at a more perfect or less perfect degree, is *their soul, their spirit*.

Let us turn back and examine critically the operation of analysis that gradually led us down from the heights of rational life to the particulate swarming of electrons. We progressed in a series of successive fragmentations. At each operation we separated two elements: an ordering principle, which is imponderable, cannot be analysed, and is synthetic—and ordered (ponderable) elements. On every occasion, as a direct result of analysis, that ordering principle disappeared. We accordingly concentrated our attention on the ordered elements, which seemed to be of a more stable nature. These in turn yielded to analysis, sacrificing a fresh order and being reduced to sub-elements. And so the process continued. Thus we have left the statue to study the grain of marble—the sensation of light to retain the vibration of the ether—cellular life to fasten onto chemical combinations, etc. In doing so, we believed that we were making our way towards what was more solid, to something that would be a non-ordered prime element. It was a hopeless search. We did, it is true, discover a certain law on which reality is built up, an hierarchical law of increasing complexity in unity. But reality itself, the supreme Thing we were trying to reach, eluded us and with each new analysis continued to move even further away, just as the light moves further away from a person who is chasing its reflexion. What we have been doing is to advance in the direction in which everything disintegrates and is attenuated: whereas the absolute, the intelligible, lies at the centre, in the direction in which everything is heightened to the point of being but one. Everything is something more than the elements of which it is composed. And this something more, this soul, is the true bond of its solidity.

One could say that the structure of things, taken individually or as a whole, *is similar to that of a cone*. A cone has an apex and a base, a centre of convergence and a zone of indefinite divergence. An observer who follows the axis of a cone as he proceeds towards the apex, finally reaches the point where all the generating lines meet and join up. A reversal of direction leads him towards an endless dissociation of the elements that make up the figure. Similarly, in our analytical exploration of the world, we have been moving towards the base of the cone, and that is why the world seemed to slip through our hands. This, however, is no permanent set-back, but rather a most important discovery. By this evidence of the increasing fragmentation of beings around us, we are at last able to determine the point in the universe at which we have arrived, to understand its structure, to set things in their proper perspective, and to decide in which direction our target is hidden. We now know what is meant by 'penetrating to the heart of things'. If we are to reach the luminous, solid, absolute zone of the world, what we have to do is not to make our way towards what lies *deepest below or furthest behind but towards what is most interior in the soul and most new in the future*. The elementary and the past are as empty of mystery as the geographical bowels of the continents and the ultimate depths of the ocean. It is a *mirage* that causes us to see the nature of things in their *origin* ('origins' recede before us incessantly, like the *horizon*). We can no more find the origin of things than *the source of a river*: '*crescit eundo*'—'its growth is in its motion'. The explanation of the world and its consistence are to be found in a higher soul of progressive attraction and solidification, without which the radical plurality of the universe would never have emerged from its dust. To the informed observer, analysis of matter reveals the priority and primacy of Spirit.

2. The 'scientific' road back to the divine centre

What methods, my friends, shall we use and what guide can we find if we are to penetrate the real in the new direction that we have just seen to be the true road of search and discovery? After descending the slope that automatically leads towards the most elementary, the most divided, the earliest in time, how can we recognise the paths that lead to the most synthetic and the newest—impossible to determine beforehand, and complicated as they are? Can we still ask science to guide us on this new journey? It has already led us to the pole at which things are dissociated; can it now lead us up to the pole at which they are supremely associated?

Many people believe, and you must often have heard it maintained, that 'science is strong enough to save us on its own'. Precisely because science has broken everything down, it holds the secret of putting it together again. Thus it has usurped the power that we used to regard as the prerogative of God. 'Look', we are told, 'at the results we have already achieved. We are able (or soon shall be able) to make the ether vibrate at our will, to construct extremely complex molecular structures that are well on the road to organic matter. One day, perhaps, we shall be able artificially to

31

create such conditions that we shall cause life to germinate as and when we wish. Why should it not be possible to lay our hands on energies that are considered even more sacred? Medical and psychological science are still groping their way in the empirical, but they have not said their last word. May we not quite possibly succeed in mastering the energies of body and soul, and so methodically free ourselves from the restrictions of our organism and spiritualise ourselves scientifically?'

We have just met, and tried to overcome, the illusion or temptation that tried to make us believe that we were nothing but matter. How are we to counter this new, spuriously scientific, view that we have become like gods? One would have to be very rash, I realise, to determine in advance a point beyond which scientific synthesis will never advance. I shall refrain, therefore, from relying on such predictions, which facts have too often belied. I shall even maintain that our duty as men is to act *as though there were no limit to our power*. Life has made us conscious collaborators in a Creation which is still going on in us, in order to lead us, it would appear, to a goal (even on earth) much more lofty and distant than we imagined. We must, therefore, help God with all our strength, and handle matter as though our salvation depended solely upon our industry.

Granting that, however, I shall add this observation, which, if properly understood, will suffice to acquit the scientific conquest of the world of any spirit of pride or insensitivity. For all the progress of science in the mastery of matter and in the art of releasing vital forces, we have no reason to fear that these advances will ever oblige us, logically, to slacken our effort; on the contrary, we may be certain that they will serve only to make the impetus of moral and religious effort assert itself in us more imperatively.

When you come to think about it, there is something impossible, and contradictory, in the attempt, like that of the Titans, to force the gates of fuller life without reference to, or contrary to, moral values. The effort towards organic unity is essentially (by structural necessity) complicated by an internal attitude of the heart and the will. *The scientific synthesis of man* (if I may put it so) *is continued just as necessarily in moral progress, as the chemical synthesis of proteins is continued in biological manifestations.* To act like Titans?—impossible. And why? (1) because synthesis that unifies *in se*$=\alpha$ virtue. (2) because synthesis that unifies *inter se*$=\alpha$ centre. We are always tempted to regard the moral governance of life, the mystical view of things, as superficial, subjective phenomena, as energies belonging to a lower physical 'stuff'. In reality, they both represent in us the direct continuation of the forces, that, under the creative influx, have built up the successive circles of the world. They are the index, the measure, the factors, of the true organic synthesis of Spirit.

The further we advance along the highways of matter towards the perfecting of our organism, the more imperative will it become for the unity our being has won to be expressed, and to be completed, in the fibres of our consciousness by the predominance of spirit over flesh, by the harmonisation and sublimation of our passions.

And the closer we come, through the diligent convergence of our efforts, to the common centre to which the elements of the world gravitate, the more will it become our duty, as conscious atoms of the universe, to submit ourselves 'constructively' to the more and more far-reaching ties, to the dominating, universal influence of this more fully known centre—and the more incumbent will be the duty of worship.

I would never dream, my friends, of deducing Christian dogmas solely from an examination of the properties our reason attributes to the structure of the world. Christ, we must add, is the plenitude of the universe, its principle of synthesis. He is therefore something more than all the elements of this world put together; in other words, although the world can justify our expectation of Christ, he cannot *be deduced from it.*

What is legitimate, and at the same time heartening, is to note, as we shall now do, how appropriately Christian views supply what we are looking for. Science, we saw, by the very impotence of its analytical efforts has taught us that in the direction in which things become complex in unity, there must lie a supreme centre of convergence and consistence, in which everything is knit together and holds together. We should be overcome with joy (which is not putting it too strongly) to note how admirably Jesus Christ, in virtue of his most fundamental moral teaching and his most certain attributes, fills this empty place which has been distinguished by the expectation of all Nature.

Christ preaches purity, charity and self-denial. But what is the specific effect of purity if it is not the concentration and sublimation of the manifold powers of the soul, the unification of man in himself? What, again, does charity effect, if not the fusion of multiple individuals in a single body and a single soul, the unification of men among themselves? And what, finally, does Christian self-denial represent, if not the deconcentration of every man in favour of a more perfect and more loved Being, the unification of all in one?

And then comes the question of Christ himself—who is he? Turn to the most weighty and most unmistakable passages in the Scriptures. Question the Church about her most essential beliefs; and this is what you will learn: Christ is not something added to the world as an extra, he is not an embellishment, a king as we now crown kings, the owner of a great estate . . . He is the alpha and the omega, the principle and the end, the foundation stone and the keystone, the Plenitude and the Plenifier. He is the one who consummates all things and gives them their consistence. It is towards him and through him, the inner life and light of the world, that the universal con-

34

vergence of all created spirit is effected in sweat and tears. He is the single centre, precious and consistent, who glitters at the summit that is to crown the world, at the opposite pole from those dim and eternally shrinking regions into which our science ventures when it descends the road of matter and the past.

When we consider this profound harmony that for us Christians links and subordinates the zone of the multiple and the zone of unity, the essentially analytical domain of science and the ultra-synthetic domain of religion, then, my friends, I believe that we may draw the following conclusions: and they are the moral of this over-long address.

1. Above all, we Christians have no need to be afraid of, or to be unreasonably shocked by, the results of scientific research, whether in physics, in biology, or in history. Some Catholics are disconcerted when it is pointed out to them—either that the laws of providence may be reduced to determinisms and chance—or that under our most spiritual powers there lie hidden most complex material structures—or that the Christian religion has roots in a natural religious development of human consciousness—or that the human body presupposes a vast series of previous organic developments. Such Catholics either deny the facts or are afraid to face them. This is a huge mistake. The analyses of science and history are very often accurate; but they detract nothing from the almighty power of God nor from the spirituality of the soul, nor from the supernatural character of Christianity, nor from man's superiority to the animals. Providence, the soul, divine life, are synthetic realities. Since their function is to 'unify', they presuppose, outside and below them, a system of elements; but those elements do not constitute them; on the contrary it is to those higher realities that the elements look for their 'animation'.

2. Thus science should not disturb our faith by its analyses.

Rather, it should help us to know God better, to understand and appreciate him more fully. Personally, I am convinced that there is no more substantial nourishment for the religious life than contact with scientific realities, if they are properly understood. The man who habitually lives in the society of the elements of this world, who personally experiences the overwhelming immensity of things and their wretched dissociation, that man, I am certain, becomes more acutely conscious than anyone of the tremendous need for unity that continually drives the universe further ahead, and of the fantastic future that awaits it. No one understands so fully as the man who is absorbed in the study of matter, to what a degree Christ, through his Incarnation, is interior to the world, rooted in the world even in the heart of the tiniest atom. We compared the structure of the universe to that of a cone: only that man can fully appreciate the richness contained in the apex of the cone, who has first gauged the width and the power of the base.

3. It is useless, in consequence, and it is unfair, to oppose science and Christ, or to separate them as two domains alien to one another. By itself, science cannot discover Christ—but Christ satisfies the yearnings that are born in our hearts in the school of science. The cycle that sends man down to the bowels of matter in its full multiplicity, thence to climb back to the centre of spiritual unification, *is a natural cycle*. We could say that it is a *divine cycle*, since it was first followed by him who had to 'descend into Hell' before ascending into Heaven, that he might fill all things. 'Quis ascendit nisi qui descendit prius, ut impleret omnia.'[3]

Lecture given in Paris, 27 February 1921

[3] After Ephesians 4. 9, 10.

CHAPTER IV

MY UNIVERSE[1]

This essay makes no claim to provide a final explanation of the world. It is not directly aimed at establishing any general theory of thought, of action and mysticism, as though the prospects it opens up had to be directly accepted in that form by all thinking people, at the expense of certain other ways of seeing things that are, rightly or wrongly, regarded as more traditional, or are more generally held. All I wish to do is to explain how I personally understand the world to which I have been progressively more fully introduced by the inevitable development of my consciousness as a man and a Christian. Reacting on my own individual nature, the truths of religion and its practice (in a process from which I feel my personal freedom has been completely excluded) have led me to the conclusions that I shall now try to express. It is this determinism (or, if you prefer the phrase) this irresistible spontaneity that matters most in what follows. The system I am putting forward will obviously be very open to criticism from the intellectual point of view, but such criticisms will be quite unable to rob it of its special value, which is that it provides an incontestable psychological witness. My philosophical skill may be greater or less, but one fact will remain permanently unchallenged: that an ordinary man of the twentieth century, because he shared as any one else would in the ideas and cares of his own time, has been unable to find the proper balance for his interior life except in a unitary concept, based

[1] This essay is the second to bear this title *My Universe*. The first dated (1918) will be included in a later volume.

upon physics, of the world and Christ—and that therein he has found unbounded peace and room for personal development.

Even in itself, this objective success has its own importance. It proves that in spite of the clumsiness and comparative inexactness of the terms I use, a spiritual urge has been trying to express itself in me, which others, later, will pin down more felicitously. I feel, indeed, that it is not I that conceived this essay: it is a man within me who is greater than I—a man whom I have recognised countless times, and always the same, close to me. For all its limitations, my experience in these last ten years has convinced me that both within and outside Christianity many more minds than we suspect are drawing nourishment from the same intuitions and the same ill-defined feelings as those that have filled my life. It has been my destiny to stand at a privileged cross-roads in the world; there, in my twofold character of priest and scientist, I have felt passing through me, in particularly exhilarating and varied conditions, the double stream of human and divine forces. In this favoured position on the frontier of two worlds I have found outstanding friends to help me develop my thought, and long periods of leisure in which to mature it and stabilise it. And because of that good fortune, I feel that I would be disloyal to Life, disloyal, too, to those who need my help, if I did not try to describe to them the features of the resplendent image that has been disclosed to me in the universe in the course of twenty-five years of reflexions and experiences of all sorts. As I said before, they will find in it no more than a rough outline. But the happiness of their lives will consist, as has mine, in working unremittingly to fill in its exact characteristics.

What makes the point of view I shall try to define so powerfully attractive, and the reasons why one can find peace in it, is the flexibility and ease with which, once we adopt it, the countless elements of the world—the physical, moral, social, and religious world—link together, fall into order and mutually illuminate one another: a process that continues indefinitely and reaches into the most intimate depths of their being. My whole 'apologetics' will consist in demonstrating this solid, natural, total coherence. I shall leave aside any discussion of particular propositions. I shall not be concerned to multiply postulates; nor shall I be at pains to pursue into their final developments the corollaries without number that will crop up as we follow the main sweep of the directive principles we shall trace in bold outline. My only concern will be to show how it is possible, by approaching the vast disorder of things from a certain angle, suddenly to see their obscurity and discord become transformed in a vibration that passes all description, inexhaustible in the richness of its tones and its notes, interminable in the perfection of its unity. If I succeed in sharing this success and making it in some small degree understood, I shall have given the best of all proofs: since the synthesis of the real is realised so effortlessly, it can contain only the truth.

I. PHILOSOPHY: CREATIVE UNION

A. FUNDAMENTAL PRINCIPLES

Before embarking on a synthetic exposition of the philosophy that supports and gives organic form to the building up of my moral and religious constructions, it may be well to bring out a number of fundamental principles or postulates in which can be seen the 'spirit' in which my representation of the universe has been conceived and in which it has developed.

1. The primacy of consciousness

Logically and psychologically, the first of these principles is the profound conviction that being is good: in other words,

a. that it is better to be than not to be;
b. that it is better to be more than to be less.

If we accept as an auxiliary principle that 'complete' being is conscious being, then we may express this principle in a clearer and more practical form, as follows:

a. That it is better to be conscious than not to be conscious.
b. That it is better to be more conscious than less conscious.

When first stated, these propositions might appear self-evident or sterile. In reality, as soon as we try to draw the ultimate conclusions from them, we see that they are big with imperative implications. And it is surprising to find, by experience, how vigorously they are often contested, both in theory and in practice, by agnostics, by pessimists, by the pleasure-seeking, and the small-minded. It may well be that it is in this basic choice between the absolute value or non-value of the fullest consciousness that the great cleavage occurs between good men or bad, the elect or the reprobate.

2. *Faith in life*

Directly side by side with this first corner-stone of my interior life—the primacy of Consciousness—I can distinguish another: Faith in life, in other words the unshakeable certainty that the universe, considered as a whole

a. Has a goal.
b. Cannot take the wrong road nor come to a halt in mid-journey.

Taken in isolation, only a pathetically insignificant proportion of the elements of the world, sad to say, turns out successfully. With absolute conviction, I refuse to extend this total contingency to the elements as a collective whole. I cannot admit that the universe is a failure. This privilege (the assurance of success) may be due to a providential transcendent action; or to the influence of a spiritual energy immanent in the whole (some soul of the world); or to a sort of infallibility which, though not accorded to isolated attempts, attaches to indefinitely multiplied attempts ('the infallibility of great numbers'); or again it may, more probably, derive from the hierarchically ordered action of these three factors at the same time; the precise reason does not matter for the moment. Before looking for any explanation of the thing, I believe in the fact that the world, taken as a whole, is assured of attaining its end, that is to say (in virtue of our first principle) of arriving at a certain higher degree of consciousness.

I believe it by inference: because, if the universe has hitherto been successful in the unlikely task of bringing human thought to birth in what seems to us an unimaginable tangle of chances and mishaps, it means that it is fundamentally directed by a power that is eminently in control of the elements that make up the universe. I believe it, too, from necessity: because, if I thought that the solidity of the substance in which I am implicated was not proof against any test, I would feel completely lost and despairing. Finally, and perhaps most of all, I believe it from love: because I love the universe that surrounds me too dearly not to have confidence in it.

3. Faith in the absolute

Since the world is a success (Principle 2) and since success consists in becoming more conscious (Principle 1), I conclude, as we have just seen, that the universe ripens within itself the fruit of a certain consciousness. If we ask what essential attribute we demand in this highest form of consciousness, in this sort of higher being, in order to be able to recognise that it is indeed a success, we shall say that it must represent a state

41

that is acquired *for ever*; in other words, we look for an absolute perfection.

It is in fact quite clear that ninety-nine men out of a hundred never explicitly ask themselves the question, 'Is life worth living?' They fail to see the problem, because life is still carrying them along automatically, just as it did the unreasoning beings who, until man, were alone in conducting the work of evolution. Logically, however, the problem is there, and we may anticipate that it will take on increasing urgency for mankind, as the work achieved by the latter becomes more arduous and valuable. Can we truly hope to create a work that will last, or are we simply building a house upon sand? With intelligence there emerged in the heart of the terrestrial world a formidable power of judging the world critically. Animals, passively and blindly, drag the great lumbering wagon of progress. Before man, in turn, can continue the common task, he can, and must, ask himself whether it is worth the suffering it entails: the toil of living, the horror of dying. And I appeal to every man who is capable of looking into the depths of his mind and heart, to consider frankly and honestly whether the only reward that can satisfy us is not the guarantee that the tangible result of our labours, through some part of itself, is gathered up in a reality where neither worm nor rust can devour it.

The demand I am now expressing may seem excessive; nevertheless I believe that it is absolutely natural to man, because I can read it so plainly in my own heart that it must, logically, be shared by all my fellows. The more I think about it, the more clearly I see that I would be psychologically incapable of making the least effort if I were unable to believe in the absolute value of something in that effort. Prove to me that one day nothing will remain of my work, because there will be not only a death of the individual and a death of the earth, but a death, too, of the universe—prove that, and you break the mainspring of all my activity. Promise my being thousands of years of personal life or of super-human usefulness in some Greater one than itself. If, at the end of that time, annihilation lies in wait for me, it is just as though death were coming upon me tomorrow: I would not lift a finger to be a better man. *Free will can be put into motion*, in the smallest matter, *only by the appeal of a definitive result*, of a '*Ktema eis aei*' —an everlasting possession—promised to its effort.

And since in actual fact (Principle 2) I cannot admit that the world is badly constructed—is physically contradictory—is incapable of feeding the hunger of the beings it has produced within itself—then I cling desperately to the certainty that life, in its totality, is directed towards the establishment of a new and eternal earth.

4. *The priority of the whole*

With what characteristics, then, shall I now picture to myself the terminal Reality, the only Reality that has value, that gathers up all that is absolute in my work and in the work of life? With those, inevitably, of an immense Unity. Since it is life in its totality, and not in its elements, that is infallible (Principle 2); and since all that is purest in the vital fluid developed by each monad must be concentrated in the fruit we look for from the growth of the world (Principle 3), the Absolute towards which we are ascending can wear only the face of the whole—a whole that is purified, sublimated, made conscious.

Gradually, thus, my faith in the value of the individual being has become more sharply defined and enriched, until it brings me sharp up against some universally awaited Reality. The intellectual process is logical. Historically, I am sure, my mind has travelled in an opposite direction. It is not I that have laboriously discovered the whole; it is the whole that has presented itself to me, imposed itself on me, through a sort of 'cosmic consciousness'. It is the attraction of the whole that has set everything in motion in me, has animated and given organic form to everything. It is because I feel the whole and love it passionately that I believe in the primacy of being—and that I cannot admit that life meets a final check—and that I cannot look for a lesser reward than this whole itself.

Philosophically and psychologically, as what follows will continually make clear, nothing in the world is intelligible except in and starting from the whole.

B. CREATIVE UNION

The various principles I have just been examining mark out the field within which we must look for a solution of the problem of life—but they do not as yet provide us with an interpretation of the world. This I have tried to work out for myself in the theory of Creative Union.

Creative union is not exactly a metaphysical doctrine. It is rather a sort of empirical and pragmatic explanation of the universe, conceived in my mind from the need to reconcile in a solidly coherent system scientific views on evolution (accepted as, in their essence, definitively established) with the innate urge that has impelled me to look for the Divine not in a cleavage with the physical world but through matter, and, in some sort of way, in union with matter.

I arrived quite simply at this explanation of things by considering the extremely puzzling relationship between Spirit and matter. If there is any fact well established by experience, it is that 'the higher the level of psychism attained, in all the living beings we know, the more closely it appears to be associated with a complex organism'. The more spiritual the soul is, the more multiple and fragile is its body. This curious law of compensation does not seem to have attracted any special

attention from the philosophers, except in so far as it has provided them with an opportunity of driving even deeper the
abyss they seek to set between Spirit and matter. It seemed to
me that far from being a paradoxical or accidental relationship, it might very well disclose to us the hidden constitution
of beings. Instead, therefore, of treating it as a difficulty or an
objection, I transformed it into the very principle by which
things may be explained.

Creative union is the theory that accepts this proposition: in
the present evolutionary phase of the cosmos (the only phase
known to us), everything happens as though the One were
formed by successive unifications of the Multiple—and as
though the One were more perfect, the more perfectly it cen-
tralised under itself a larger Multiple. For the elements associated by the soul in a body (and thereby raised to a higher
degree of being), 'plus esse est plus cum pluribus uniri'—'to be
more is to be more fully united with more'. For the soul itself,
for the principle of unity, 'plus esse est plura unire'—'to be
more, is more fully to unite more'. For both, to receive or to
communicate union is to undergo the creative influence of
God, 'qui creat uniendo'—'who creates by uniting'.

These expressions should be carefully weighed if they are
not to be taken in a wrong sense. They do not mean that the
One is composed of the Multiple, i.e. that it is born from the
fusion in itself of the elements it associates (for in that case
either it would not be something created—something completely new—or the terms of the Multiple would be progressively decreasing, which contradicts our experience). They
simply express this fact, that the One appears to us only in the
wake of the Multiple, dominating the Multiple, since its
essential and formal act is to unite.—And this allows us, in
consequence, to lay down a fundamental principle, as follows:
'Creative union does not fuse together the terms which it
associates (for does not the bliss it confers consist precisely in

45

becoming one with the other while remaining one's own self?).
It preserves the terms—it even completes them, as we see in
living bodies, where the cells are the more specialised, the
higher in the animal series the being to which they belong.
Every higher soul *differentiates* more fully the elements it
unites.'

The laws of creative union have been abundantly verified in
the field open to our historical or experimental research. In
consciousness gradually rising up on an ever wider and taller
pyramid of animate matter, we see the most objective and
most satisfactory expression of the real to be found in the
whole range and depth our senses can attain. But what the
human mind delights in is to try to extend around itself the
harmony of its outlook upon things, beyond the circle of direct
vision. The law of recurrence represented by creative union
lends itself with wonderful flexibility to this blessed enter-
prise. And the main lines of the organisation it introduces into
the dim mass of the most distant past and the most ultimate
future may be described as follows.

At the lower limit of things, too deep for any of us to penetrate, it discloses an immense plurality—complete diversity
combined with total disunity. This absolute multiplicity
would, in truth, be nothingness, and it has never existed. But
it is the quarter from which the world emerges for us: at the
beginning of all time, the world appears to us rising up from
the Multiple, impregnated with and still bedewed with the
Multiple. Already, however, since *something* exists, the work of
unification has begun. In the first stages in which it becomes
conceivable to us, the world has already been for a long time at
the mercy of a multitude of elementary souls that fight for its
dust in order that, by unifying it, they may exist. There can be
no doubt about it—what we call inorganic matter is certainly
animate in its own way. Complete exteriority or total 'trans-
sience', like absolute multiplicity, is synonymous with

nothingness. Atoms, electrons, elementary particles, no matter what they be (so long as they are something outside ourselves) must possess the rudiments of immanence; in other words, they must have a spark of spirit. Before physical and chemical conditions on earth made possible the birth of organic life, the universe either had no existence in itself, or already constituted a nebula of consciousness. Every unity of the world, provided it be a natural unity, is a monad.

In the world of matter, monads unite to an inconsiderable degree or imperfectly. That is why they are so inordinately stable in comparison with living beings properly so called. In animals they unite to a more marked degree—sufficiently to become extremely fragile, but still not enough to resist the disintegration that lies in wait for them. Only in man, so far as we know, does spirit so perfectly unite around itself the universality of the universe that, in spite of the momentary dissociation of its organic foundation, nothing can any longer destroy the 'vortex' of operation and consciousness of which it is the subsisting centre. The human soul is the first fully formed purchase point that the Multiple can fasten onto as it is drawn up by the Creation towards unity.

Such, all around us, is the position in the universe. Like a sphere that radiates from innumerable centres, the material world can today be seen by us as suspended from the spiritual consciousness of men. What has creative union to teach us about the balance and the future of this system? It gives us formal warning that the world we see is still profoundly unstable and incomplete. Unstable, because the millions of souls (living or departed) now included in the cosmos form an uneasy multiple, that, for mechanical reasons, must have a centre if it is to hold together. Incomplete because, while it represents a weakness, their very plurality is a strength and a source of hope for the future—that being the demand for or the anticipation of a later unification in spirit. In consequence, the

47

whole weight of past evolution forces us men to look higher than ourselves in the series of spiritual development. If it is our own souls that give solidity to the infra-human world, the human world, in turn, cannot be conceived except as supported by conscious centres vaster and more powerful than ours. Thus we are gradually introduced (from the more multiple to the less multiple) to the concept of a first, supreme centre, an omega, in which all the fibres, the threads, the generating lines, of the universe are knit together. From the point of view of the completion of the movement it governs it is a centre still in formation—a potential centre; but it is already a real centre, too, since without its attractive force operating here and now, the general stream of unification would be unable to raise up the Multiple.

The picture, then, is perfectly clear: in the light of creative union the universe assumes the form of a huge cone, whose base expands indefinitely to the rear, into darkness, while its apex rises up and concentrates ever further into the light. Throughout the whole, the *same* creative influence makes itself felt, but always in a more conscious, more purified, more complex form. Initially, it is only vague affinities that set matter in motion; soon, however, the pull of the living can be felt: in lower forms it is an almost mechanical process, but in the human heart it becomes the infinitely rich and formidable power of love. Finally, at a still higher level, the passion is born for the realities that lie above the circles of man, realities in which in some vague way we feel we are immersed. Science is necessarily chiefly concerned with studying the material arrangements that are successively effected by the progress of life. In so doing, it sees only the outer crust of things. The true evolution of the world takes place in souls and in their union. Its inner factors are not mechanistic but psychological and moral. That, as we shall again have occasion to note, is why the further, physical, developments of mankind—the true continuations, that is, of its planetary, biological, evolution—will be found in the increased consciousness obtained by the activation of psychical forces of unification.

C. SOME COROLLARIES OF CREATIVE UNION

If we accept the above picture of the universe, it is surprising to see with what ease a whole series of propositions, most valuable for the better understanding of the world and for making better use of it, emerge as consequences of creative union.

1. As the first of these corollaries, this fundamental principle stands out with all the emphasis of a truth of the first order, that 'All consistence comes from Spirit.' In that we have the very definition of creative union. Our direct, undigested experience of the world would incline us to the contrary view. The solidity of the inorganic and the fragility of the flesh tend to stimulate the belief that all consistence comes from matter. We must resolutely reverse this crude view of things: physics, in fact, is busily abolishing it by demonstrating the slow disappearance of substances that we used to regard as indestructible. The truth is that nothing holds together except as the result of a synthesis, which means, in short, however lowly the synthesis, by a reflexion of Spirit. The materialist philosopher, therefore, who looks at a lower level than soul for the solid principle of the universe, grasps no more than dust that slips between his fingers. And, as a further consequence, the fleshly man, too, who tries to find the object of his passion in any other way than by aiming at raising up his own being, without, that is, trying to produce a sort of new, richer, and loftier soul from the union of two living beings— that man, too, is introducing into his attempt at adhesion an irremovable principle of separation. Every new step in material enjoyment takes him further from his love.

49

Throughout the vast network of universal multiplicity, from the humblest element to the most sublime, from Nature's most material constructions to the most refined products of our thought, from the smallest association of monads to the most immense organic wholes, 'Everything holds together from on high.'

2. Everything holds together from on high. From this it follows, first, that every reality around us, no matter how spiritual it be, can be indefinitely broken down into terms of a nature lower than its own. Living organisms can, each in their own particular way, be reduced to physical and chemical elements; scientific hypothesis into more or less crude facts; the free act into determinisms; intuition into syllogisms; faith into reasons for belief; sacred inspiration into human lucubrations. Each new degree, however, of reduction to the multiple (of materialisation) allows a soul to escape. Analysis, that admirable and powerful tool for dissecting the real, leaves us with terms that become ever less intelligible and more impoverished. It discloses to us the law that governs the construction of things; but when its work is done, what is left, far from giving us the stable essence of the world, is an ever closer approximation to nothingness.

3. Once again, everything holds together from on high. Above all, this principle hallows the Kingship of Spirit; but at the same time it thereby preserves and ennobles matter. Indeed, even if it is Spirit that constantly carries matter along and supports it in the ascent towards consciousness, it is matter, in return, that enables Spirit to subsist by constantly providing it with a point upon which to act, and supplying it with nourishment. As we said before, the Spirit that sustains everything, itself has no reason for its being and consistence, does not 'hold together', except by 'causing to hold together'. Its sublimity and richness are tied up with an organic multiplicity that it embraces in its 'solid aspect'. The purity of a being's

50

spiritual peak is in proportion to the material breadth of its base.

4. In the system of creative union, moreover, it becomes impossible to continue crudely to contrast Spirit and matter. For those who have understood the law of 'spiritualisation by union', there are no longer two compartments in the universe, the spiritual and the physical: there are only *two directions* along one and the same road (the direction of pernicious pluralisation, and that of beneficial unification). Every being in the world stands somewhere on the slope that rises up from the shadows towards the light. In front of it, lies the effort to master and simplify its own nature; behind, the abandonment of effort in the physical and moral disintegration of its powers. If it goes forward, it meets the good: everything is Spirit for it. If it falls back, it meets nothing on its road but evil and matter. Thus an infinite number of steps are spaced out between absolute evil (that is, nothingness, the total plurality to which everything reverts) and the Supreme Good (that is, the centre of universal convergence towards which everything tends); these steps are, no doubt, separated by a number of 'landings' (like that, for example, which marks off animal from man, or man from angel), but they nevertheless represent one general movement, and to each step there corresponds a particular distribution of good and evil, of Spirit and matter. What is evil, material, for me, is good, spiritual, for another advancing by my side. And the climber ahead of me on the mountain would be corrupted if he used what gives me unity.

Matter and Spirit are not opposed as two separate things, as two natures, but as two directions of evolution within the world.

5. Thus those innumerable difficulties vanish which every philosophy comes up against that tries to reconstruct the world from isolated elements (from the monad) instead of

affirming in principle the fundamental and substantial unity of the universe. The mutual influence of Spirit and matter, the interaction of beings, the knowledge of the 'external' world, are insoluble questions only because we give ourselves the spurious and impossible problem of trying to understand the whole through fragments of the whole, without introducing, to help us, the properties that are peculiar to the whole (as though a natural whole were not more than its parts). These philosophical cruxes are seen to be illusory as soon as it is understood that there is ultimately one single physical reality developing in the cosmos, one single monad. There is no need to look for a 'bridge' between natures or things in a universe in which unity (and, in consequence, complete inter-influence) is the state of equilibrium towards which beings tend as they become spiritualised.

Minds that are warped by an exaggeratedly intellectualist and geometric ontology will no doubt be astounded by such an idea: the idea of incomplete and hierarchically arranged substances linked together in sequence, in accordance with a uniform organic law, and finding in this relationship the fulness of their individual differentiation and power to act. It will shock those who like to divide the real into substances (all equally substantial) and accidents. I can only be sorry for those who feel in this way. True wisdom consists in retaining the obscurities of the world at the points at which they do in reality appear, and not in shifting them artificially on the pretext of respecting principles that are only apparently evident—or that hold good only for a universe that has reached the term of its evolution. When a mystery is put in its correct setting, it becomes as fruitful as the most thoroughly understood truths. This is so in the case of the principle accepted by creative union that 'in natura rerum', 'in nature', there is no completed substance, no substance, accordingly, existing in isolation; but every substance is held up by a series of Substances-of-Substance that support one another, step by step, up to the Supreme Centre at which everything converges.

Without these two notions of 'incomplete substance' and 'Substance-of-Substance', all philosophy remains incoherent and handicapped. Once, on the other hand, these notions are accepted, everything is lucidly explained, and everything around us stands out with extraordinary clarity—not only in metaphysics but also, and perhaps even more so, in morality and religion.

II. RELIGION: THE UNIVERSAL CHRIST

The prospects opened up by the application of the law of recurrence which we have called Creative Union, are convincing enough when we are concerned with the representation of the universe's past; they become somewhat fantastic when we turn to the mysteries of the future. To admit that human monads are elements of a higher organic synthesis, to accept that they are destined to form the body of a soul more spiritual than our own, so outstrips our imagination that we feel we must find some positive evidence upon which to base such disturbing extrapolations.

Many non-Christian mystics have not hesitated, trusting to their own desires and natural predilections, to cast themselves into the delectable abyss of belief in a soul of the world. The Christian, for his part, has only to reflect upon his creed to find in the Revelation he accepts the unlooked-for realisation of the dream to the threshold of which philosophy logically leads him. What I hope to do in this chapter is to show that Christianity so truly takes on its full value in virtue of the ideas contained in creative union that that theory, instead of being regarded as a philosophy which the Christian view confirms and then takes the place of, should more rightly be called a philosophical extension of faith in the Incarnation.

Let us, for brevity's sake, give the name of omega to the upper cosmic term disclosed by creative union. All that I shall have to say about it may be reduced to three points:

A. The revealed Christ is identical with omega.

B. It is inasmuch as he is omega that he is seen to be attainable and inevitably present in all things.

C. And finally it was in order that he might become omega that it was necessary for him, through the travail of his Incarnation, to conquer and animate the universe.

A. CHRIST IS IDENTICAL WITH OMEGA

In order to demonstrate the truth of this fundamental proposition, I need only refer to the long series of Johannine—and still more Pauline—texts in which the physical supremacy of Christ over the universe is so magnificently expressed.[2] I cannot quote them all here, but they come down to these two essential affirmations: 'In eo omnia constant' (Col. 1. 17), and 'Ipse est qui replet omnia' (Col. 2. 10, cf. Eph. 4. 9), from which it follows that 'Omnia in omnibus Christus' (Col. 3. 11)—the very definition of omega. I am very well aware that there are two loopholes by which timid minds hope to escape the awesome realism of these repeated statements. They may maintain that the cosmic attributes of the Pauline Christ belong to the Godhead alone; or they may try to weaken the force of the texts by supposing that the ties of dependence that make the world subject to Christ are juridical and moral, the rights exercised by a landowner, a father or the head of an association. As regards the first subterfuge, all I need to do is to refer to the context, which is categorical: even in Col. 1. 15 ff, St Paul quite obviously has in mind the theandric Christ; it was

---

[2] See, in particular, St Paul: Rom. 8. 18 sq.; 14. 7, 9; 1 Cor. 4. 22; 6. 15 sq.; 10. 16; 12. 12 sq.; 15. 23–9; 39 sq.; 2 Cor. 3. 18; 4. 11; 5. 4; 19; Gal. 3. 27, 28; Eph. 1. 10, 19–23; 2. 5, 10, 13, 14; 3. 6, 18; 4. 9, 12, 13, 16; Phil. 2. 10; 3, 10, 11, 20–1; Col. 1. 15–20, 28; 2. 9, 10, 12, 19; 3. 10; 1 Thess. 4. 17; Heb. 2. 7–8. (Ed.)

in the Incarnate Christ that the universe was pre-formed. As regards the weakened interpretation of the Apostle's words, I dismiss it simply because it is less in conformity with the spirit of St Paul as it animates the body of his Epistles, and less, too, in conformity with my general view of the world. However, I have given up hope of converting those who reject my version. I have, in fact, become convinced that men include two irreconcilable types of minds: the physicalists (who are 'mystics') and the juridicists. For the former, the whole beauty of life consists in being organically structured; and in consequence Christ, being pre-eminently attractive, must radiate physically.[3] For the latter, being is embarrassing as soon as it disguises something vaster and less patient of definition than our human social relationships (considered from the point of view of their artificial content). Christ, accordingly, is no more than a king or a great landowner. These (the juridicists), logically inconsistent with their theology of grace, will always understand 'mystical' (in 'mystical body') by analogy with a somewhat stronger family association or association of friends. The physicalists, however, will see in the word mystical the expression of a hyper-physical (super-substantial) relationship—stronger, and in consequence more respectful of embodied individualities, than that which operates between the cells of one and the same animate organism. The two types of mind will never understand one another, and the

---

[3] This reasoning, which assumes that the *Reality* of Christ is gradually *defined by the increasing requirements* of *our ideal*, is legitimate. It is not because Christ is the most beautiful being that is, absolutely, possible (does that, in any case, mean anything?), but because he is the most beautiful relatively to us (since it is he who fulfils us), that we are justified in saying: 'This is more beautiful than that: therefore it is this, and not that, which belongs to Christ.' The difficult problem for Christian thought (and the stimulus behind the evolution of dogma) is precisely to maintain at all times in Christ the plenitude of these three attributes: being at the same time historic, universal and ideal. To be 'ideal' is a way of being universal; it is to be capable of meeting the aspirations of mankind of all periods. One might also say, reciprocally, that Christ must be universal because our ideal demands his universality.

choice between the two attitudes must be made not by reasoning but by insight. For my own part, it has been made, irrevocably and as long as I can remember. I am a physicalist by instinct: and that is why it is impossible for me to read St Paul without seeing the universal and cosmic domination of the Incarnate Word emerging from his words with dazzling clarity.

This is the point we must bear in mind: in no case could the cosmos be conceived, and realised, without a supreme centre of spiritual consistence. It would be most unreasonable to imagine the separate creation of an atom or a group of monads, not only in view of the particular principles expressed in creative union, but simply as a matter of sound metaphysics. The goal before Creation and attained by Creation is in the first place the whole, and then, in and after the whole, all the rest. On any hypothesis, if the world is to be thinkable it must be centred. The presence, therefore, at its head, of an omega has nothing to do with the fact of its 'supernatural elevation'. What gives the world its 'gratuitous' character is precisely that the position of universal centre has not been given to any supreme intermediary between God and the universe, but has been occupied by the Divinity himself—who has thus introduced us 'in et cum Mundo' into the triune heart of his immanence.

That, then, will suffice to make my theological position clear. Now to look more closely, in its physical potency, at the Mystery of Christ.

B. THE INFLUENCE OF CHRIST-OMEGA.
THE UNIVERSAL ELEMENT

Having noted that the Pauline Christ (the great Christ of the mystics) coincides with the universal term, omega, adumbrated by our philosophy—the grandest and most necessary attribute we can ascribe to him is that of exerting a supreme physical influence on every cosmic reality without exception.

As we have already seen, in the light of pure reason, nothing in the universe is intelligible, living, and consistent except through an element of synthesis, in other words a spirit, or from on high. Within the cosmos all the elements are dependent upon one another ontologically, in the ascending order of their true being (which means of their consciousness); and the entire cosmos, as one complete whole, is held up, 'informed', by the powerful energy of a higher, and unique, Monad which gives to everything below itself its definitive intelligibility and its definitive power of action and reaction.

So: it is that energy, 'qua sibi omnia possit subjicere' (Phil. 3. 21), which we must unhesitatingly attribute to the Incarnate Word, if we are not to allow a world to assume greater dimensions, to overflow its limits, around the figure of Christ—a world that would be more beautiful, more majestic, more organic, and more worthy of worship than Christ. Christ would not be the God of St Paul, nor the God of my heart, if, looking at the lowliest, most material, created being, I were unable to say, 'I cannot understand this thing, I cannot grasp it, I cannot be fully in contact with it, except as a function of him who gives to the natural whole of which it is a part its full reality and its final determined form.' Since Christ is omega, the universe is physically impregnated to the very core of its matter by the influence of his super-human nature. The presence of the Incarnate Word penetrates everything, as a universal element. It shines at the common heart of things, as a centre that is infinitely intimate to them and at the same time (since it coincides with universal fulfilment) infinitely distant.

The vital, organising, influence of the universe, of which we are speaking, is essentially grace. We can see, however, from the point of view of creative union, that this wonderful reality of grace must be understood with a much greater intensity and width of meaning than is normally attributed to it. Theologians, in order to make it clear that grace does not make us cease to be ourselves, include it in the humble category of 'accidents', along with sonority, colours, or good spiritual qualities. Enslaved to their philosophical categories they make it (in contrast with the universal practice of the mystics) into something infra-substantial.[4] This, we say, is because they cannot bring themselves to accept the existence of incomplete substances, hierarchically ordered, in other words, Substances-of-Substance. We, on the other hand, take this new class of beings as the foundation of our explanation of the world, and in consequence will say that grace is no less intimate to ourselves, no less substantial, than humanity. It is, indeed, even more so. By Baptism in cosmic matter and the sacramental water we are more Christ than we are ourselves—and it is precisely in virtue of this predominance in us of Christ that we can hope one day to be fully ourselves.

So much, then, for the physical intensity of grace. As for the scope of its 'morphogenic' influence, it is boundless. In fact, since Christ is omega, he does not restrict his organising activity simply to one zone of our being—that of sacramental relationships and the 'habitus' of virtues. To enable himself to unite us to him through the highest part of our souls, he has had to undertake the task of making us win through in our entirety, even in our bodies. In consequence, his directing and informing influence runs through the whole range of human works, of material determinisms and cosmic evolutions. By convention, we call these lower processes in the universe 'natural'. In reality, by virtue of Christ's establishment as head of the cosmos, they are steeped in final purpose, in

---

[4] While St Thomas says that grace is a quality (an 'accident') since it is the splendour of the soul, at the same time he speaks of it (and, it would seem, by preference) as a new nature which allows man to participate 'according to a certain likeness, in the divine nature, by a sort of generation or new creation' (S. Th. I, II, q. 110, art. 4). (Ed.)

supernatural life, even to what is most palpable in their reality. Everything around us is physically 'Christified', and everything, as we shall see, can become progressively more fully so.

In this 'pan-Christism', it is evident, there is no false pantheism. What normally vitiates pantheism is that, by setting the universal centre below consciousness and below the monads, it is obliged to conceive 'omega' as a centre of intellectual dissociation, of fusion, of unconsciousness, of relaxation of effort. As soon as the true perspective is restored, as we have done, all these objectionable features disappear. Because our omega, Christ, is placed at the upper term of conscious spiritualisation, his universal influence far from dissociating, consolidates; far from confusing, differentiates; far from allowing the soul to wallow in a vague, supine, union, it drives it ever higher along the hard and fast paths of action. The danger of false pantheisms has been removed, and yet we retain the irreplaceable strength of the religious life that the pantheists unjustly claim as their own.

All around us, Christ is physically active in order to control all things. From the ultimate vibration of the atom to the loftiest mystical contemplation; from the lightest breeze that ruffles the air to the broadest currents of life and thought, he ceaselessly animates, without disturbing, all the earth's processes. And in return Christ gains physically from every one of them. Everything that is good in the universe (that is, everything that goes towards unification through effort) is gathered up by the Incarnate Word as a nourishment that it assimilates, transforms and divinises.[5] In the consciousness of this vast two-way movement, of ascent and descent, by which the development of the Pleroma (that is, the bringing of the universe to maturity) is being effected, the believer can find astonishing

[5] In short, Christ, understood in this sense, is the milieu in which and through which the (abstract) attribute of *the divine immensity* is concretely realised for us.

illumination and strength for the direction and maintenance of his effort. Faith in the universal Christ is inexhaustibly fruitful in the moral and mystical fields. But before we devote a special chapter to studying the practical conclusions of our system, we must consider by what stages was realised and by what mechanism is constituted, the wonderful cycle that dynamically links together, in their whole history, Heaven and earth, Spirit and matter.

C. THE ANIMATION OF THE WORLD BY THE UNIVERSAL CHRIST

The concentration of the Multiple in the supreme organic unity of omega represents a most arduous task. Every element, according to its degree, shares in this laborious synthesis, but the effort called for from the upper term of unification has necessarily had to be the hardest of all. That is why the Incarnation of the Word was infinitely painful and mortifying—so much so that it can be symbolised by a cross.

The first act of the Incarnation, the first appearance of the Cross, is marked by the plunging of the divine Unity into the ultimate depths of the Multiple. Nothing can enter into the universe that does not emerge from it. Nothing can be absorbed into things except through the road of matter, by ascent from plurality. For Christ to make his way into the world by any side-road would be incomprehensible. The Redeemer could penetrate the stuff of the cosmos, could pour himself into the life-blood of the universe, only by first dissolving himself in matter, later to be reborn from it. 'Integritatem Terrae Matris non minuit, sed sacravit'—'he did not lessen, but consecrated the integrity of Mother Earth'. The smallness of Christ in the cradle, and the even tinier forms that preceded his appearance among men, are more than a moral lesson in humility. They are in the first place the application of a law of birth and, following on from that, the sign of Christ's definitively taking possession of the world. It is because Christ was 'inoculated' in matter that he can no longer be dissociated from the growth of Spirit: that he is so engrained in the visible world that he could henceforth be torn away from it only by rocking the foundations of the universe.

It is philosophically sound to ask of each element of the world whether its roots do not extend into the furthest limits of the past. We have much better reason to accord to Christ this mysterious pre-existence. Not only 'in ordine intentionis' but 'in ordine naturae', 'omnia in eo condita sunt'—'all things are contained in him', not only 'in the order of intention' but also 'in the order of nature'. The endless aeons that preceded the first Christmas are not empty of Christ, but impregnated by his potent influx. It is the ferment of his conception that sets the cosmic masses in motion and controls the first currents of the biosphere. It is the preparation for his birth that accelerates the progress of instinct and the full development of thought on earth. We should not, in our stupidity, be horrified because the Messiah has made us wait so interminably for his coming. It called for all the fearsome, anonymous toil of primitive man, for the long drawn-out beauty of Egypt, for Israel's anxious expectation, the slowly distilled fragrance of eastern mysticism, and the endlessly refined wisdom of the Greeks—it called for all these before the flower could bloom on the stock of Jesse and of mankind. All these preparations were cosmically, biologically, necessary if Christ was to gain a footing on the human scene. And all this work was set in motion by the active and creative awakening of his soul, in as much as that human soul of his was chosen to animate the universe. When Christ appeared in the arms of Mary, what he had just done was to raise up the world.

Then there began for him a second phase of effort and suffering on the Cross: the only phase we can in some degree understand, because it is the only one which corresponds to what we are now conscious of ourselves: the phase, after that of 'Kenosis' in matter, of human 'co-feeling'. If Christ was to conquer human life, to dominate it with his own life, he had to do more than stand in juxtaposition to it: he had to assimilate it, in other words to test it, savour it, subdue it in the depths of his own self. We would, therefore, be failing to understand his historical existence, we would be distorting and profaning it, if we did not see in it a vast hand to hand struggle between the principle of supreme unity and the Multiple it was engaged in unifying.

In the first place, Christ experienced in himself the *individual* human heart, the heart that constitutes our agony and our bliss. But in Christ there was not simply a man—there was man; not only the perfect man, the ideal man—but the total man, the man who gathered together, in the depth of his consciousness, the consciousness of all men. In virtue of this, Christ's experience had to extend to the universal. Let us try to gather together in one single ocean the whole mass of passions, of anticipations, of fears, of sufferings, of happiness, of which each man represents one drop. It was into this vast sea that Christ plunged, so as to absorb it, through all his pores, in his entire person. It was this storm-tossed sea that he diverted into his mighty heart, there to make its waves and tides subject to the rhythm of his own life. That is the meaning of the ardent life of Christ, Christ the source of all our good, of Christ as he prays; and therein lies the unfathomable secret of his agony, and the incomparable virtue, too, of his death on the Cross.

In itself, death is a failure and a stumbling-block. It is the blind revenge taken by the insufficiently mastered elements on the soul that hampers their autonomy. It comes into the world as the direst of weaknesses, the most bitter of our enemies. Nevertheless, in spite of this initial taint, it can be put to good use, and in an unexpected direction, by the processes of creative union. For a being, to die normally means to sink back into the Multiple; but it can also be for it the reshaping that is indispensable to its entry under the dominion of a higher soul. The bread we eat appears to be decomposed within us, but it nevertheless becomes our flesh. Could there not also be dissociations in the course of which the elements would never cease to be dominated by a unity that breaks them up only to give them a new form? In every union the dominated term becomes one with the dominant only by first ceasing to be itself. In the case of the definitive union with God in omega, we can see that if the world is to be divinised it must, in each one of us and in its totality, lose its visible form. From the Christian point of view, that, in virtue of the death of Christ, is the life-giving function of human death.

In order that physiological death (the remains, in us, of the domination of the Multiple) could be transformed into a means of union, it was necessary—physically necessary—for the monads doomed to suffer death to learn to accept it with humility and love, and above all with immense trust. We had, intellectually and vitally, to overcome the horror with which destruction fills us. By subjecting himself to the trial of individual death, by his blessed acceptance of the death of the world, Christ effected this reversal of our outlook and fears. He vanquished death. He gave it, physically, the value of a metamorphosis: through which the world, with him, entered into God.

And then Christ rose again. We are often too inclined to regard the Resurrection as an isolated event in time, with an apologetical significance, as some small individual triumph over the tomb won in turn by Christ. It is something quite other and much greater than that. It is a tremendous[6] cosmic event. It marks Christ's effective assumption of his function as

[6] Père Teilhard uses the English word. (Ed.)

the universal centre. Until that time, he was present in all things as a soul that is painfully gathering together its embryonic elements. Now he radiates over the whole universe as a consciousness and activity fully in control of themselves. After being baptised into the world, he has risen up from it. After sinking down to the depths of the earth, he has reached up to the heavens. 'Descendit et ascendit ut impleret omnia' (Eph. 4. 10). When, presented with a universe whose physical and spiritual immensity are seen to be ever more bewildering, we are terrified by the constantly increasing weight of energy and glory we have to attribute to the son of Mary if we are to be justified in continuing to worship him, it is then that we should turn our thoughts to the Resurrection.

Like the Creation (of which it is the visible aspect) the Incarnation is an act co-extensive with the duration of the world. How, then, here and now, is the influence of the universal Christ transmitted to us? Through the Eucharist; but by the Eucharist understood, once again, in its universal power and realism.

Christian faith has always recognised and joyfully worshipped in the Eucharist the natural continuation of Christ's redemptive and unitive act. But can one say that in that regard (any more than in many others) the piety of the faithful is fully satisfied by the explanation of the growing attraction towards Communion given in the currently accepted formulas? The Host (that is, the real presence of Christ) is still too often presented as a localised, external, element to which our approach, even if we are daily communicants, is, in a word, no more than temporary—and in exile from which, therefore, we are almost permanently obliged to live. If we are worthily to interpret the fundamental place the Eucharist does in fact hold in the economy of the world; if we are to meet the legitimate demands of those who, because they love Christ, cannot bear to be for one moment excluded from him, then I believe we must accord an important place in Christian thought and prayer to the real, and physical, extensions of the Eucharistic Presence.

The Host, it is true, is in the first place, and primarily, the fragment of matter to which, through transubstantiation, the Presence of the Incarnate Word attaches itself among us, that is to say in the human zone of the universe. The centre of Christ's personal energy is really situated in the Host. And, just as we rightly give the name of 'our body' to the local centre of our spiritual radiation (though that does not perhaps necessarily mean that our flesh is more ours than is any other matter) we must say that the initial Body of Christ, his *primary Body*, is confined to the species of bread and wine. Can Christ, however, remain contained in this primary Body? Clearly, he cannot. Since he is above all omega, that is, the universal 'form' of the world, he can attain his organic balance and plenitude only by mystically assimilating (and we have already explained the hyper-physical sense to be attached to that word) all that surrounds him. The Host is like a blazing hearth from which flames spread their radiance. Just as the spark that falls into the heather is soon surrounded by a wide circle of fire, so, in the course of centuries, the sacramental Host—for there is but one Host, ever growing greater in the hands of a long succession of priests—the Host of bread, I mean, is continually being encircled more closely by another, infinitely larger, Host, which is nothing less than the universe itself—the universe gradually being absorbed by the universal element. Thus when the phrase 'Hoc est Corpus meum' is pronounced, 'hoc' means 'primario' the bread; but 'secundario', in a second phase occurring in nature, the matter of the sacrament is the world, throughout which there spreads, so to complete itself, the superhuman presence of the universal Christ. The world is the final, and the real, Host into which Christ gradually descends, until his time is fulfilled. Since all time a single word and a single act have been filling the universality of things: 'Hoc est corpus meum'. Nothing is at work in creation except in order to assist, from near at hand or from afar, in the consecration of the universe.

If this truth is properly understood, it is the firmest basis and most powerful stimulus we can find for our effort to attain the good and achieve progress.

III. MORALITY AND MYSTICISM:
PRE-ADHESION

From the point of view of creative union the law and the ideal of all good (whether moral or physical) are expressed in a single rule (which is also a hope): 'in all things to work for, and accept, the organic unity of the world.' To work for it, in as much as it requires for its consummation the co-operation of its elements: to accept it, in as much as its realisation is primarily the effect of a synthetic domination, superior to our own power. Confirmed, exactly defined, and transfigured by faith in the Incarnation, this rule of action takes on incomparable urgency and delightfulness: and it is readily expressed, too, in any number of immediate and practical obligations. We shall see that for the Christian who is dedicated to the unification of the world in Christ, the whole task of the interior moral and mystical life may be reduced to two essential and complementary processes: to conquer the world, and to escape from it. Each is a natural consequence of the other, and they represent two allied forms of one and the same urge: to come together with God through the world.

A. THE CONQUEST OF THE WORLD. DEVELOPMENT

One thing I think has been made clear: the initial impulse that sets the Multiple in motion towards unity, the energy at

the source that animates the whole sequence of cosmic unification and spiritualisation, is the magnetic force of omega.
Without that gratuitous appetite for Being, without that pre-
venient zest for union, the mechanism of the universe would
remain immobile, the elements of the world would never
emerge from their infinitely tenuous plurality. But once the
'concept' of an omega has kindled in the monads the desire to
meet with Spirit, they develop a restless mobility and feel
themselves impelled towards activity. God's first wish, expressed by the surge of life within us, is that his creatures
should increase and multiply.[7] And to be true to him they
must first develop themselves and conquer the world.

The nature of this obligation is often understood by minds
we have called 'juridicist' as an obedience due to the more or
less extrinsic and arbitrary order of a master. To hear some
people speak, you would think that the only reason why man
had to work was to give proof of his good will. All that we are
called on to produce here below is a fragile vessel, soon to
crumble into powder. But no matter: it is not the material
results of man's work that counts, but the obedience he has
shown in producing things that are useless.

When, however, the Christian discovers the grand truth
that Christ is omega, there is a wonderful transformation of
this sterile and disheartening attitude. If Christ is omega,
nothing is alien to the physical building up of his universal
body. Look no matter where, in the endless series of material
or living processes that are constantly at work in the world, at
any activity you please: however humble and unobtrusive it
be, it still—so long as it is carried out with a view to unification

---

[7] The multiplication of living beings is not a return to plurality, but the constitution of a Multiple of a higher order (new matter) destined to maintain a new
soul. However progressive and spiritualising it may be, this multiplication still
remains a danger: by creating 'the mob' it introduces into the world a new
chance (more serious than the earlier ones) for imprudent emancipation and
revolt. It is the risk inherent in being.

—creates an atom of fuller being, and that atom is immediately assimilated for all time, through all that is best in it, by the total Christ. Every process of material growth in the universe is ultimately directed towards spirit, and every process of spiritual growth towards Christ. From this it follows that whether the work to which I am tied by the circumstances of the present moment be commonplace or sublime, tedious or enthralling, I have the happiness of being able to think that Christ is waiting to receive its fruit: and that fruit, we must remember, is not only the intention behind my action but also the tangible result of my work. '*Opus ipsum, et non tantum operatio.*'

If this hope is justified, the Christian must be active, and busily active, working as earnestly as the most convinced of those who work to build up the Earth, that Christ may continually be born more fully in the world around him. More than any unbeliever, he must respect and seek to advance human effort—effort in all its forms—and above all the human effort which is aimed more directly at increasing the consciousness (that is, the being) of mankind; by that I mean the scientific quest for truth, and the organised attempt to develop a better social nexus. In those aims, those who love the universal Christ should never let themselves be outstripped in hope and boldness. No one, in fact, has so many reasons as they have for believing in the universe, and for launching an assault upon it in order to make it their own.

There is no need to fear that in pursuing their own development and that of the world, such men will become attached to the earth. As they mature in the earth they become, on the contrary, detached from it. On the one hand (this is a point to which we shall return) what they are seeking for in matter and life's progress is not directly either matter or life: it is solely the divine Light that dances over the transparent folds of the real, and which we cannot reach unless we launch ourselves boldly into the deep waters of cosmic becoming. On the other hand (and precisely in virtue of the hidden dynamism instilled into things by the unity that dominates them) the very effort they make to grasp the world has the immediate consequence of causing them gradually to withdraw from it.

B. DETACHMENT FROM THE WORLD. DIMINISHMENT

1. *Death through action*

The vital logic of action is such that we cannot conquer our own selves and increase our stature except through a gradual death of ourselves. To act worthily and usefully, we have seen, is to achieve unity. But to be united is to be transformed into a greater than oneself. Ultimately, then, to act is to leave behind the material, the immediate, the self-centred, and so advance into the universal Reality that is coming to birth. All that rather involved way of putting it is simply a way of expressing the most commonplace and frequently met experience of our lives—the painfulness of hard work.

Nothing is more excruciating than effort, and that is true of spiritual effort too. If you ask the masters of the ascetical life what is the first, the most certain, and the most sublime of mortifications, they will all give you the same answer: it is the work of interior development by which we tear ourselves away from ourselves, leave ourselves behind, emerge from ourselves. Every individual life, if lived loyally, is strewn with the outer shells discarded by our successive metamorphoses— and the entire universe leaves behind it a long series of states in which it might well have been pleased to linger with delight, but from which it has continually been torn away by the inexorable necessity to grow greater. This ascent in a continual sloughing off of the old is indeed a way of the Cross.

Spurred on by this impulse continually to leave himself behind in order to arrive at the term of his own self (the term, that is, of the world), the man who faithfully follows the ascending slope of the universe,[8] becomes progressively less concerned with his individual success (as an individual). At first he sought to approach perfection for his own sake, but later he becomes enamoured of loftier, vaster and more enduring realities, closer to the absolute, than his personal reality. A terrestrial ideal with which is closely associated a cause to be defended, a natural beauty—human or cosmic—to contemplate and win —these are the brilliant things behind which the Divinity is revealed to him and becomes progressively tangible for him. In virtue of the structure of the world (that is, of universal convergence towards Christ), the man who acts in a religious spirit ends by almost entirely dismissing himself from his mind. He soon comes to see himself as no more than a sort of conscious atom dedicated to a great task; and if he is to come up to the measure of that task he is forced to rely on increasingly sublime energies. After having been, perhaps, primarily sensitive to bodies, and primarily concerned with the tangible accretions procured for the world by material means, he tends, irresistibly swept along, to become interested only in the progress of soul. He is inclined to restrict his concern to spiritual forces and to trust exclusively to them (to prayer, for example, which provides a link with God—to purity, which knits together the fibres of the soul—to charity, which organically associates human monads). And at the same time the need to act and assert himself is imperceptibly transformed into a thirst for submission and self-giving.

2. Death through passivity

We see, then, what creative union entails. The element of Christ (and that is what each one of us is) has hardly begun to

---

[8] Ascending because of the attraction of omega.

be conscious of itself deep in our nature, before the eager desire to meet the Principle which dominates it is simultaneously kindled in it. And that is why, when we have worked, faithfully and industriously, to develop ourselves, we look so anxiously around us for an almighty hand that we can worship, *si forte attractent Eum.*

It is an infinite delight, no doubt, to the Christian, to grow greater for Christ (and the more so in that it is Christ himself, in the very depths of our being, who seeks to be born and grow greater in our bodies and souls: our ardour, our zest for life, is itself, indeed, a passivity). But this growth has ultimately no meaning or value except in so far as it allows us to provide the divine contact with a firmer grip. It is that contact we now have to effect. Where shall we find it? Is it, as we no doubt wonder, mysterious, infrequent, grudging, distant? If we are to offer ourselves to it, must we make our way into some extremely deep zone? The reality is much simpler and lovelier than we imagine. 'In eo vivimus, movemur, et sumus'. Christ operates, he exerts his living pressure, on the believer who can act and believe rightly, through all the surface and depth of the world. It is he who encompasses us and moulds us, at every moment, through all the passivities and restrictions of our lives.

Here we must be most careful to distinguish the two phases in the implementing, in the world around us, of the will of God: in other words, in the animation of secondary causes by the influx of the universal Christ. In itself, and directly, our bondage to the world—particularly those forms of it that irk us, that diminish us, that kill us—is not divine, nor is it in any way willed by God. It represents that portion of incompleteness and disorder which mars a creation that is still imperfectly unified. In so far as they are such, these forms of bondage are displeasing to God; and, in a first stage, God fights with us (and in us) against them. One day he will triumph; but,

71

because the duration of our individual lives is out of all proportion to the slow evolution of the total Christ, it is inevitable that we shall never, during our time on earth, see the final victory. Almost every moment brings another check to our effort to grow, undermines it—and sooner or later we shall all experience decline and death. Christ, nevertheless, can never be overcome. If, then, we ask how the almighty power, which is his in virtue of his cosmic function, of saving and beatifying the elements of his Body in growth, will in some way re-establish itself, the answer is that it will do so by a remarkable *transformation*. The Incarnate Word masters the limitation and diminishments that the general progress of the cosmos does not allow him to remove (in the same way as a skilful sculptor masters the shortcomings of his marble), by integrating them (though without changing them) in a higher spiritualisation of our beings. That is why, when we have fought to the bitter end to develop ourselves and win through, and find ourselves halted, beaten, by the forces of this world, then, *if we believe*, the power with which we clash so agonisingly suddenly ceases to be a blind or evil energy. Hostile matter vanishes. And, in its place, we find the divine Master of the world who 'under the species and appearance' of each and every event, moulds us, empties us of our self-love, and penetrates into us. '*Oportet illum crescere, nos autem minui.*'[9] This is the most magnificent of the prerogatives of the universal Christ: the power to be operative in us, not only through the natural impulses of life but also through the shocking disorders of defeat and death.

This wonderful transformation, let me insist, is not effected immediately nor without our co-operation. We are justified in resigning ourselves to evil only when we have first resisted it with all the strength at our command. *If we are to succeed in*

---

[9] 'He must grow greater, but we must grow less', adapting what St John the Baptist said of Christ and himself (John 3. 30). (Ed.)

submitting to the will of God we must first make a very great effort.
God is not to be found indiscriminately in the things that
thwart us in life or the trials we have to suffer, but solely *at the
point of balance* between our desperate efforts to grow greater
and the resistance to our domination that we meet from outside. In that area of equilibrium, however, he is born only *in
so far as we believe* that he is: '*Diligentibus*, omnia convertuntur
in bonum'—'*for those who love*, all things are transformed
into good.'

But once this double stipulation has been made (our loyal
effort and our trust) the most obscure and most hateful part
of the world becomes the most luminous and divine of all.
Beneath the countless servitudes and disappointments of the
world the formative power of Christ can be discerned, mould-
ing us and substituting himself for us.

Sometimes Christ makes our sorrows and mishaps serve to
direct us along loftier paths, in which we improve ourselves *by
experience*: think of all the saints who became saints through
having been worsted in some terrestrial field; but often, again,
our losses and our failures do not seem to be compensated by
any appreciable advantage, even spiritual. It is then, most of
all, that we must hold firm to our trust in God. The world can
attain God, in Christ Jesus, only by a complete recasting in
which it must *appear* to be entirely lost, with *nothing* (of the
terrestrial order) *that our experience could recognise as compensation*. When such a death, whether it be slow or rapid, takes
place in us, we must open our hearts wide to the hope of
union: never, if we so will it, will the animating power of the
world have mastered us so fully.

C. THE MYSTICAL MILIEU – COMMUNION

Action and acceptance: these two halves of our life—this in-
haling and exhaling of our nature—are transfigured and

clarified for us in the rays of creative union. Whatever we do, it is to Christ we do it. Whatever is done to us, it is Christ who does it. Christian piety has always drawn strength from these words of universal and constant union; but has it, I wonder, always been able, or been bold enough, to give to that union the forceful realism that, since St Paul first wrote these words, we have been entitled to expect?

Once we make up our minds to take the words of Revelation literally—and to do so is the ideal of all true religion—then the whole mass of the universe is gradually bathed in light. And just as science shows us, at the lower limits of matter, an ethereal fluid in which everything is immersed and from which everything emerges, so at the upper limits of Spirit a mystical ambience appears in which everything floats and everything converges.

And in this rich and living ambience, the attributes, seemingly the most contradictory, of attachment and detachment, of action and contemplation, of the one and the multiple, of spirit and matter, are reconciled without difficulty in conformity with the designs of creative union: everything becomes one by becoming self.

When I am working for the progress of the universe, so to prepare for Christ a body less unworthy of him, I am attaching myself to the world and to myself—but at the same time I am detaching myself from it, because this world itself, divorced from Christ and his light, seems to me full of darkness and has no power to attract me. The light ahead eludes me as I move from zone to zone, and if I am to follow it I must reach those regions where activity is the most far-reaching in its ambitions, the least self-centred in its outlook, the most chaste in its dreams of union.

During this ascending progress, things are still sharply defined for me. It is through them, in fact, that Christ becomes tangible to me—it is through them that he reaches me and has contact with me. I cannot, therefore, dispense with them; and, logically, I shall be in the forefront of the realists, since I cannot apprehend God except by completing the world. Nevertheless, if I am still untiring in my pursuit of created beings and my attempt to perfect them, it is solely in the hope that in them I may find the divine Fire which plays in them as though in the purest crystal. Is it not in the heavenly Jerusalem that the elements of the new earth will be so transparent, reflecting so brilliantly, that nothing, seemingly, will subsist but the rays, materialised in us, of God's glory?[10]

Mystical writers disagree as to whether action must precede contemplation as a preparation for it, or whether it springs from contemplation, as a superabundant gift from God. I must confess that such problems mean nothing to me. Whether I am acting or praying, whether I am painfully opening up my soul by work, or whether God takes possession of it through the passivities that come from within or without, I am equally conscious of finding unity. It is in this consciousness that the mystical activity 'formally' resides. Whether I am actively impelled towards development by the sensibly perceptible aspirations of my nature, or painfully mastered by material contacts, or visited by the graces of prayer, in each case I am equally moving in the mystical Milieu. *First and foremost*, I am in Christo Jesu; it is only *afterwards* that I am acting, or suffering, or contemplating.

If we had to give a more exact name to the mystical Milieu we would say that it is a Flesh—for it has all the properties the flesh has of palpable domination and limitless embrace. When given life by the universal Christ, the world is so active and has such warmth, that not one of the impressions I receive from it fails to 'inform' me a little more with God. Like a

---

[10] 'Et civitas non eget sole neque luna . . . nam claritas Dei illuminavit eam, et lucerna eius est Agnus'—'and the city has no need of sun or moon . . . for the glory of God is its light, and its lamp is the lamb' (Apoc. 21. 23).

powerful organism, the world transforms me into him who animates it. 'The bread of the Eucharist', says St Gregory of Nyssa, 'is stronger than our flesh; that is why it is the bread that assimilates us, and not we the bread, when we receive it.' At the same time, however, this transformed world, this universal flesh, so close at hand and so tangible, can only, it seems to us, be apprehended in the far distance of sublimity. When passion is lofty and noble, the man and woman who come together meet only at the term of their spiritual growth. This law of human union is the law of our cosmic union. Christ holds us by the most material fibres of nature. Nevertheless, we shall possess him perfectly only when our personal being, and the world with it, have step by step reached the full limit of their unification.

It would be illogical to regret these long delays, the slowness of these processes. They are not in the first place an arbitrary trial or a punishment. They are an expression of the very law of the evolution of spirit. Christ is born upon the unified Multiple. That is why there is an infinity of zones, of circles, of dwelling-places, in his universal and luminous Flesh. The mystical Milieu fades away for everything that, through diminution of action and through self-love, redescends the slope of the Multiple. On the other hand (as being already divine) it grows brighter around everything that strives to rise up and be unified.

Moralists are often at a loss to justify (notably in Art) certain human works which the absolute, fixed, teachings of moral theology censure, but which human life obviously cannot do without. The reason is that they have not understood (cf. p. 51) that good and evil are not two departments, but two directions, in human activity. For you, a more spiritual man, it would as a general rule be reprehensible to stoop to certain sights and pleasures, and certain doubts—even though in some cases you might still need to give the roots of your soul new nourishment by so doing. But for many others, these realities that are left behind you lie, on the contrary, on the road to the light. These latter must therefore pass through these lower elements before they can climb higher. Every reality, for every person and every thing, encloses a dynamism, some form of Christ's magnetism; and nothing (individuals no more than the whole) can attain spirit *except along a determined path through matter*. No stage in the journey can be by-passed. Each must be taken in turn; and it would be extremely difficult to say to what depths below us the roots of spirit still extend. You, then, who flatter yourself that you live by the light alone, you are nevertheless nourished, without suspecting it, by the cruder sap that others are humbly refining in the depths of matter. The Flesh of Christ is fed by the whole universe. The mystical Milieu gathers up everything that is made up of energy. Nothing in the world is completely lacking in power, and nothing is rejected, except that which turns its back on the unification of spirit.[11]

In the eyes of the believer, the universe is seen to be a flesh. This fact brings us back to the considerations with which earlier (p. 65) we ended our reflexions on the universal Christ. What the mystical vision precisely does—and what the mystical act assists—is to disclose the universal and sacramental consecration of the world. *To consecrate the world by a complete faith* that makes him see in the infinite network of secondary causes the organic influence of Christ; to *enter into communion with the world* through a complete *loyalty* in grasping every opportunity of growing greater and in accepting every

---

[11] One cannot over-emphasise the fact that the sanctification of souls, however personal it may be, is still essentially collective. We are spiritualised by being carried along by the spiritualisation of all things. We are united to Christ by entering into communion with all men. We shall be saved by an option that has chosen the whole. And the beatific vision will be not so much an individual vision as a specific act of the Mystical Body, the Divine revealing itself to each one of us through the eyes of Christ.

summons to die—it is to this, ultimately, that the interior life may be reduced for the Christian.

The man who has understood this immense simplicity of things, who has heard beneath the universal din the one unique Note—*that man possesses the world*. Intimately involved in things though he is through his eager efforts to complete them and understand them, he does not, even so, share their instabilities. He impinges upon them, but he attains God through them. And in the plenitude that flows over him from this *pre-adhesion* to God in All, he cannot say which is the more precious of these two graces: that he has found Christ to animate matter, or matter to make Christ universally tangible.[12]

IV. HISTORY: THE EVOLUTION OF THE WORLD

Hitherto, we have been primarily concerned to bring out the intimate structure of the world, without trying to picture to ourselves the main lines of its history in an over-all view. As a summary and an application of the theories of creative union, we should now try to determine the characteristics assumed, in their light, by the internal evolution of the cosmos in which we are involved.

A. THE PAST

However far back we look into the past, we see the waves of the Multiple breaking into foam as though they emerged from a negative pole of being. The fringes of our universe, we have seen, are lost in material and unconscious plurality. To our experience this ocean is as boundless as the material space that surrounds us. We often hear the expression, 'the first

---

[12] The only difference, but the essential difference, that distinguishes these remarks from the usual theory currently accepted of the Presence of God, is that, from the point of view adopted here, the Presence of God reaches the elements of the world *exclusively through (and in) the body of Christ.*

moment of the world'—it is a very mistaken way of putting it, and to look for such a thing would be a waste of time. The creative act is not interpolated in the chain of antecedents. It is imposed upon the universe taken in its full extension and full duration. It is impossible, therefore, for the elements of the world to emerge from the world, to reach even a lower limit of the world. It is impossible for it to conceive (logically) a physical term for the world, or even (rationally) to imagine the isolated creation of an element of the world apart from or outside it.[13] All around us, until it is lost to sight, radiates the net of spatial and temporal series, endless and untearable, so closely woven in one piece that there is not one single knot in it that does not depend upon the whole fabric. God did not will individually (nor could he have constructed as though they were separate bits), the sun, the earth, plants, or Man. He willed his Christ;—and in order to have his Christ, he had to create the spiritual world, and man in particular, upon which Christ might germinate;—and to have man, he had to launch the vast process of organic life (which, accordingly, is not a superfluity but an essential organ of the world);—and the birth of that organic life called for the entire cosmic turbulence.

At the beginning of the perceptible world what existed was the Multiple; and that Multiple was already rising up, like one indissociable whole, towards spirit under the magnetic influence of the universal Christ who was being engendered in it.

This ascent was slow and painful; for from that moment the Multiple was, through something in itself, evil.

---

[13] Père Teilhard was always to remain sceptical of the ability of experimental science to demonstrate and date, even approximately, the beginning of the world. Can our reason, working back through the course of history, armed with the Aristotelian notion of efficient causality 'get hold of a "natural beginning", a natural "zero", a vanishing point in the past (outside time and space) which is the form of "beginning" assumed by an expanding universe? . . . I very much doubt it.' St Thomas, from another point of view, was also doubtful: he maintained that it was possible for reason to prove the creation, but it could not prove that the world had not been created *ab aeterno*. (Ed.)

Whence did the universe acquire its original stain? Why are we obliged in some way to identify evil and matter, evil and determinisms, evil and plurality? Is it only because, in relation to our souls, the lower zones of the universe and of union are a country that has been left behind—that is therefore forbidden —to fall back into which is to be corrupted? Or is it not, rather, as the Bible would seem categorically to assert, because the original Multiple was born from the dissociation of an already unified being (the First Adam), with the result that, in this present period of history, the world is not rising up towards Christ (the Second Adam) but resuming its ascent.[14]

Whichever hypothesis is accepted, that Evil[15] pluralised the world as a consequence of a culpable act—or that the world (because it is plural, evolutionary) produced Evil, at the very first instant, as an object produces its shadow[16]—in either case creative union has the particular characteristic of being a redemptive union. God seems to have been unable to create without engaging in a struggle against evil at the same time as against the Multiple.

We spoke earlier (p. 60) of the historical circumstances of the Incarnation and Redemption. Let us, then, pass through this period of the world's evolution, since it is reasonably clear to us, and peering out over the prow of our ship try, as though in a dream, to pierce the darkness of the night that is very gradually growing brighter as it sails through the world. 'Custos, quid de nocte?'

---

[14] In this case, before the present phase of evolution (of spirit from matter) there would be a phase of involution (of spirit in matter), a phase that obviously could not be known to experience, since it would have developed in another direction of the real.

[15] There is *only one Evil* = disunity. We call it 'moral' when it affects the free zones of the soul. But even then (like Good, moreover, which 'unites') it is still *physical in essence*.

[16] Evil, the scholastics say, is a privation of being—for man, a rejection of the perfection demanded by his spiritual nature. (Ed.)

B. THE FUTURE

It is indeed black as we look ahead. And there are no stars to
help us when we want to fix the position of the universe. One
thing, however, would appear to be certain. The noise of the
waves we hear is not simply the irregular crashing of the
rollers against the sides of our vessel: we can distinguish, too,
the characteristic hiss of our bow-wave. We may be somewhat
uncertain of the land towards which we are driving; but no
matter—we are not, in any case, an object drifting at random.
Things have a definite direction. We are pressing ahead, and
we are making good progress.

The learned may smile, or be angered, to hear us speak of
progress. They may smugly enumerate the scandals of the
present day, or argue about original sin, to prove that nothing
good can come from the earth. We may disregard these pessimists, who seem never to have questioned history, or reason,
or their own hearts. But have they the faintest suspicion, these
men, that their scepticism will end logically in making the
world unintelligible, and in destroying our capacity to act?
Deny that consciousness is better than unconsciousness. Deny,
too, that if man is to act he must know that his effort has some
use—and in so doing you will have denied the necessity of progress. But you will at the same time have destroyed, with your
theories, our true reasons for living.

We who, in the labyrinth of organic evolutions, recognise no
clue other than the gradual concentration of psychic faculties;
we who do not consider that fuller being is to be found directly
in comfort or in virtue, but in the increasing domination of the
world by thought (in other words in an increasing force for
Evil as much as for Good); we who believe that work is not
worth-while if nothing is to live *for ever* of the product of our
hands—we believe in progress, and we recognise it around us
in the extension of scientific discoveries, in the planning of
collective organisms, in the awakening of humanitarian feel-

81

ings and sympathy with the universal. 'All that', we are told, 'is quantitative progress, extra bits of knowledge'. 'True qualitative and organic progress', we answer. 'Because evolution seems to have reached a point at which its progress is made no longer in the individual human body (for this has reached maturity) but in the human soul, and still more, maybe, in the collectivity of human souls, from this you conclude that it has come to a halt. It has done nothing of the sort.' *Every increase of consciousness inevitably transforms* the monads and the world *in their physical being*. The fantastic enlargement, therefore, of our view of the cosmos as presented to our senses, the incessant multiplication of 'unitary' relationships in every order of things, inevitably represent an *entitative* aggrandisement of the universe. The unification that is being developed so intensely in our time in the human spirit and the human collectivity *is the authentic continuation of the biological process that produced the human brain.*

That is what creative union means.

Where then, should we apply our effort today, if it is to be as effective as possible? In which quarter is the real getting ready to yield to our pressure? Without any doubt, in the direction of unanimous quest for truth.

It would be premature immediately to abolish the vigorous, even though too brutal, expressions of warlike strength. We still need more and more powerful guns, ever larger warships, to provide material for our assault on the world. But we may well anticipate and hope that these instruments of domination and conquest will gradually be replaced by weapons that are equally powerful but will operate in a much wider and more spiritual field. In this century, human beings are still absorbed in their concern to supply their bodies with food and to find the best way of distributing their huge and growing population over the surface of the globe. Their attention is still diverted by the pleasure of cataloguing the things that Nature offers them most immediately and putting them to good use. But this period will be only a phase. Sooner or later, society will become organised. The easily won novelties of the earth will be exhausted. Men will then become more distinctly aware of the essential need of knowledge if they are to have fuller being; they will find themselves faced with vaster and more urgent problems, expressed in clearer terms; and then they will at last associate in a common quest, as eagerly as they are now doing to pile up money and slaughter one another. Intellectual research will no longer be a diversion for the dilettante, something for which the amateur has a taste. It will have taken on the dignity of a primal collective function. When mankind has become conscious of *its isolation* in the cosmos, and is threatened by collective dangers, it will *have to discover or die.*

It is thus that the age of science will open for the world. And science, in all probability, will be progressively more impregnated by mysticism (*not* in order *to be directed,* but in order *to be animated, by it*). Impelled by the logic of effort and the hidden dynamism of matter towards ever more universal hopes—realising, with pitiless clarity, the absurdity of carrying on with a human task that has no future—that portion of mankind that is following the upward road will concentrate continually more exclusively on the search for, and the anticipation of, a God; and never will Christ have found in Creation a more magnificent capacity for either loving or hating him. The truth is that forced against one another by the increase in their numbers and the multiplication of their interrelations—compressed together by the activation of a common force and the awareness of a common distress—the men of the future will form, in some way, but one single consciousness; and since, once their initiation is complete, they will have gauged the strength of their associated minds, the immensity of the universe, and the straitness of their prison, this consciousness will be truly adult and of age.

May we not imagine that at that moment, a truly and totally human act will be effected for the first time, in a final option—the yes or no as an answer to God, pronounced individually by beings in each one of whom the sense of human freedom and responsibility will have reached its full development?

It is by no means easy to picture to ourselves what sort of event the end of the world could be. A sidereal catastrophe would be a fitting counterpart to our individual deaths, but it would entail the end of the earth rather than that of the cosmos—and it is the cosmos that has to disappear.

The more I think about this mystery, the more it appears to me, in my dreams, as a 'turning-about' of consciousness—as an eruption of interior life—as an ecstasy. There is no need to rack our brains to understand how the material vastness of the universe will ever be able to disappear. Spirit has only to be reversed, to move into a different zone, for the whole shape of the world immediately to be changed.

When the end of time is at hand, a terrifying spiritual pressure will be exerted on the confines of the real, built up by the desperate efforts of souls tense with longing to escape from the earth. This pressure will be unanimous. Scripture, however, tells us that at the same time the world will be infected by a profound schism—some trying to emerge from themselves in order to dominate the world even more completely —others, relying on the words of Christ, waiting passionately for the world to die, so that they may be absorbed with it in God.

It is then, we may be sure, that the Parousia will be realised in a creation that has been taken to the climax of its capacity for union. The single act of assimilation and synthesis that has been going on since the beginning of time will then at last be made plain, and the universal Christ will blaze out like a flash of lightning in the storm clouds of a world whose slow consecration is complete. The trumpets of the angels are but a poor symbol. It will be impelled by the most powerful organic attraction that can be conceived (the very force by which the universe holds together) that the monads will join in a head-long rush to the place irrevocably appointed for them by the total adulthood of things and the inexorable irreversibility of the whole history of the world—some, spiritualised matter, in the limitless fulfilment of an eternal communion—others, materialised spirit, in the conscious torment of an endless decomposition.

At that moment, St Paul tells us (1 Cor. 15. 23 ff), when Christ has emptied all created forces (rejecting in them everything that is a factor of dissociation and superanimating all that is a force of unity), he will consummate universal unification by giving himself, in his complete and adult Body, with a finally satisfied capacity for union, to the embrace of the Godhead.

Thus will be constituted the organic complex of God and world—the Pleroma—the mysterious reality of which we cannot say that it is more beautiful than God by himself (since God could dispense with the world), but which we cannot, either, consider completely gratuitous, completely subsidiary, without making Creation unintelligible, the Passion of Christ meaningless, and our effort completely valueless.

Et tunc erit finis.

Like a vast tide, Being will have engulfed the shifting sands of beings. Within a now tranquil ocean, each drop of which, nevertheless, will be conscious of remaining itself, the astonishing adventure of the world will have ended. The dream of every mystic, the eternal pantheist ideal, will have found their full and legitimate satisfaction. 'Erit in omnibus Deus.'

Tientsin, 25 March 1924

CHAPTER V

THE PHENOMENON OF MAN[1]

One by one the different compartments of the world are coming under the unifying influence of science. From nebulae to atoms, from electricity to organic matter, the chief natural associations of unity and energy are now being brought into a common central perspective. Man is almost alone in having so far escaped this systematising of the world in terms of history and energy. We have, it is true, a comparative Anatomy and an Anthropology to study our body in its relation to animals; but their investigations are directed towards what is lowest and oldest in us, and therefore less characteristic. We have, too, a Psychology, a Linguistics, a Sociology, Political Economy, Human Geography and so on, to deal with the problems raised by the world of reflective activities; but these disciplines, however closely modelled their vocabulary and methods may be on those of the laboratory, still form a closed group, outside Nature. They treat man as a small separate cosmos, isolated from the rest of the universe. Any number of sciences concern themselves with man, but man, in that which makes him essentially human, still lies outside science.

Nevertheless, we have only to think for a moment of the tremendous event represented by the explosion of thought on the surface of the earth to be quite certain that this great episode is something more than a part of the general system of Nature: we have to accord to it a position of prime importance,

[1] Not to be confused with the essay under the same title which was written in 1930, and is included in *The Vision of the Past* (Collins, London and Harper & Row, New York, 1966, Ch. XI). Père Teilhard used the same title again for his longest and most important book (1938).

from the point of view both of using and of understanding the motive forces of the universe.

The reflexions that follow are aimed at suggesting a standpoint from which the sciences of man may be integrated with science in such a way as to extend its true scope. Mankind represents a 'natural phenomenon' in the cosmos—a phenomenon *sui generis*—a cardinal phenomenon; and, as such, it deserves to be the basis of a supreme branch of science—even at the cost of a certain general re-orientation of our outlook. It is this that I want to bring to your attention, realising, too, that we must now confine ourselves to a strictly experiential plane.

1. *The scientific reality of the Phenomenon of Man*

What makes it difficult for us to see Man as a natural phenomenon (as we see light or simple bodies) is not so much, it would seem, the very special nature of the energies that appear at his level, as the angle from which we see them.

We have become accustomed to thinking that a phenomenon is the more physical (objective, real) the more it resides in an element that is more universal in extension, or corresponds more completely to an effect of great numbers. The supreme science, for us, is the science of the ether and of atoms: in other words of a universe in which the centres (in so far as they exist) appear only as material for statistical laws, in masses and from outside. Biology itself has hitherto been regarded as a science only in so far as it believes it can discover in the organic world general pressures and collective determinisms which are reflexions of those found in matter. We may say that our present physics of matter and life (if indeed we can yet speak of a physics of life) is completely orientated in the opposite direction from the individual—from, that is, the spontaneous and conscious.

The sciences of mankind must necessarily develop in a dia-metrically contrary direction. As soon as we begin to deal with the human world, *our* world, it is the atom (which in this case means the person) that, for reasons of scale and personal interest, becomes the centre of our concern and study. Over-all realities cease to be noted or are relegated to the back-ground. In the field of human problems there is a complete reversal of the perspective of physics, and it is on the individual —and in consequence on the aspects of freedom and interior experience—that attention is fixed; it is these, accordingly, which govern our enquiries.

At the present moment, the sciences of man and the science of Nature direct their study of the real in two different direc-tions. It is this that gives their respective objects the paradoxical appearance of belonging to two distinct universes. And it is this, and only this, that has to be corrected if we are to succeed in seeing the Phenomenon of Man as natural scientists and physicists. All we have to do is to look at mankind, not through man's eyes, in isolated units and from within, but through those of a distant observer, in wholes, and from outside: it will immediately take on an appearance, if not the same as, at any rate akin to, that of all the other magnitudes of which the cosmos is the assembly.

A first step in the training of our vision consists in noting, in the world of man, behind the screen of social relationships beyond which our attention does not normally penetrate, the recognisable continuation of the principal laws that govern life in its infra-human zones. The law of irregularity in growth: progress is effected, for each special form, in leaps and spasmo-dically, now here, now there, sometimes rapidly, sometimes slowly. The law of birth: every idea or method of working or new form of association is produced by the enlargement and differentiation of a restricted nucleus, in which potentialities scattered in the human milieu are suddenly actualised. The

88

law of substitution: no unit or social institution advances indefinitely along the line of a given improvement: it soon falls
a victim to relative immobility, and its place is taken by another group. And so the process continues. Adaptation, muta-
tions, heredity, parallelisms, correlation, orthogenesis: there
is not a single rule nor a single phenomenon extracted by
biology from the study of the general movements of organic
matter for which we cannot find an equivalent in the human
social complex. And that complex itself, taken as a whole, discloses with increasing clarity strange analogies which oblige us
to treat it as a single organic object. We can observe the great
ethnic groups seeking one another out and fusing together.
Currents, both material and human, that embrace the whole
earth, are being produced within this mass. Minerals, fuels,
cereals, financial systems, books, concerts, scientists, business
men, politicians, elements without number, are fermenting
and being set into motion under the influence of and within
this active world-wide envelope. Like some sap or blood they
feed a society whose most spiritual life is becoming daily dependent on a progressively more complex general inter-
change. *The gradual establishment and functioning of mankind are
realities which we can see as having continuity with the general
development of the rest of life*: that is a first factual step in seeing
the Phenomenon of Man.

Let us take one further step and try to see mankind from
even further away. Let us close our eyes to what is distinctly
vital or individual in it, and concentrate on distinguishing
(rather as in the case of a liquid or gaseous mass) the over-all
movement of the elements. We shall find that the world, so
wonderfully spontaneous, so apprehensible and coloured by
human relationships, when they are observed at our own scale,
draws over itself, at the distance we have adopted, the impersonal and geometric veil of a new matter. Nothing but the ebb
and flow, the hum, of a vast multitude seen from a great

height. A constant pattern of births and deaths, and accidents, revealed by statistics. Pressure of peoples upon unoccupied areas. Pressure of minds on the boundaries, continually forced back, of impotence and ignorance. Affinities between individuals and nations. Mobs that can be led or are simply inert. Hardening and anchylosis of institutions. Balance, tensions, or internal resonances of the thinking mass. All these facts suggest to us that *great numbers*, with their possibility of expression in mathematical form and their tyranny, but with their vast resources, too, of accumulated energies and of richly productive probings,—that great numbers, *at a certain level, govern the general movements of human society*—and in consequence make it an object whose study belongs not simply to biology but to physics itself.

We should not find anything surprising in this alliance. The various disciplines of the universe, from physics to zoology, are tending more and more to link together as different chapters of one and the same great history. They are enquiring into the mechanism, the phases and the continuation of one and the same immense process: the development of the universe. We are finding that from one end of the experiential field to the other only one single vast Phenomenon is taking place. Man cannot lie outside that Phenomenon. It must, therefore, be possible to study him as a Phenomenon. *If we are to see the collapse of the wall that improperly divides the sciences of man from the sciences of Nature, there is ultimately no more simple, nor more radical way of doing so than to become conscious of the unity of cosmic evolution.*

2. *The specific nature of the Phenomenon of Man*

The mechanical or biological analogies we have just enumerated have already been noted often enough in the world of man; but it must be confessed that the interpretation placed on these resemblances has hitherto been so unfortunate that it has served to strengthen rather than to overcome the anthropocentric prejudices that tend to keep man in isolation from the other objects of science. We even still see society compared without any reservations to some great machine, or to some huge animal.

This undesirable dissociation arises from the failure to make the essential correction that must always be applied to our views each time we try to follow any line of reality through a new circle of the universe. The world is completely transformed from one circle to another. It undergoes an interior enrichment and recasting. On every occasion, in consequence, it presents itself to us in a new state, in which the sum of its earlier properties is partly retained and partly given a new form. This is what is forgotten by too many people who argue for (or against) evolution without even, it would seem, having understood the notion of transformation.

From this it follows that, depending on whether we are dealing with association of atoms, cells, or of animals, or of human individuals, the laws that govern affinity between elements and the nature of their interconnexions, are all similar to one another and yet are different. We should neither divide them from one another nor class them all together. It is illogical, for example, to conceive the earth as a machine, an animal, or a person; but it would be equally mistaken to deny the effect of the convergent advances of all our knowledge. This is to cause us to see ever more clearly that the thinking envelope of the earth (as well as the merely living envelope) is not simply an aggregation or a moral unity, but also an organic whole *sui generis*—a whole, moreover, to which nothing is precisely comparable but itself. And that gives us sufficient warrant for including man and his appearance among the phenomena of Nature.

In order to express the modes of being and acting that are

proper to the whole so defined, we must, it is clear, generalise our ways of thinking and aim at the acquisition of new and higher concepts. Surely such widening of intellectual categories is the finest effort the mind can make, and, in the light of the success it achieves, the most justified? What at first comes as a shock to the mind, is later accepted as a familiar piece of mental furniture, and becomes a principle directing valuable research. We have only to think, for example, of the appearance of irrational or incommensurable quantities in geometry.

Thus, to see the Phenomenon of Man is not simply to recognise the cosmic nature (the cosmic stuff) of social facts, in other words their involvement in the general historical development of the world; it is at the same time to appreciate and effect the transposition that must be applied to the organico-physical laws and concepts established first for the world of inorganic matter and then for that of vitalised matter, when we enter the world that has been given a new form by the specifically human power of reflexion, in other words, *the hominised world.*

3. *The fundamental importance of the Phenomenon of Man*

No sooner has man been reintegrated (with the requisite precautions, but in the quality of a true element) in the structure of the world, than he begins, in the eyes of science, to assume immense value. As soon as he is no longer regarded as a sort of epi- or para-phenomenon, he can only be, both qualitatively and quantitatively, a phenomenon of the first order in the universe. That is the third of the observations to which I now want to draw attention.

In the first place, *qualitatively*, man displays, to a special degree—which makes it easy to study—a certain particular energy in the world—the extreme term, in our experience, of what we might call the psychic current of the universe. Just, for example, as the exceptional intensity of the activity of radium has introduced physics to a universal property of matter, so (by virtue of the predominance assumed in the human field by the phenomenon of interior spontaneity) consciousness, even in its highest form which is freedom, is seen to be a factor that has cosmic value. Inapprehensible in the world of atoms, negligible at times in the world of organic beings, in the world of man the psychic becomes decisively the principal phenomenon. It must, therefore, be accepted by science as a scientific fact. This, it seems, cannot be disputed; and I believe that it would remain demonstrably true, even if the considerations that follow were to be left out of account.

By the very fact that it represents the distinct emergence of a universal property, the Phenomenon of Man acquires an unbounded *quantitative* value. But we may say more than this. Humanity (and this is one of its most unusual physical aspects) evolves in such a way as to form a natural unity whose extension is as vast as the earth. Our concern with the ordinary business of men prevents us from appreciating the significance of this tremendous event. And yet it is taking place under our very eyes. From day to day the human mass is 'setting'; it is building itself up; it is weaving around the globe a network of material organisation, of communication and of thought. Submerged as we are in this process, and accustomed to regard it as non-physical, we pay little attention to it. Suppose that we at last come to look at it as we would a crystal or a plant: we immediately realise that, through us, the earth *is engaged in adding* to its lithosphere, its atmosphere, its biosphere, and its other layers, one more envelope—the last and the most remarkable of all. This is the thinking zone, the 'noosphere'. Looked at from the angle of the globally elaborated result of its evolution, the Phenomenon of Man is 'telluric' in order. Its spatial dimensions coincide with those of the planet: its temporal dimensions, too. Is not man naturally in solidarity with the earth, has he not authentically emerged from the general history of the earth? The Phenomenon of Man, we were saying a moment ago, has enabled science, rather as radioactivity does, to read the secret of the elemental driving forces of the world. We now see that it takes on the amplitude (in extension) and the depth (in duration) of geological events. Mankind, to repeat, but with fuller understanding, an expression we have already used earlier, is indeed the 'hominised' earth—we might even say 'hominised' Nature.

This hominisation of the world (and this is the note on which I would like to end) is seen to be allied to a very strange characteristic, which suggests that there is something to be discovered scientifically in man that is even more interesting than the manifestation of a cosmic property or the product of a sidereal evolution: it is *irreversible*. However far back we may trace it, the phenomenon of consciousness seems to have been becoming always more generalised on earth and more marked. In spite of the accumulated improbabilities that its progress presupposes, the psychic has continually been increasing in our world; and what can be seen in mankind today is precisely its climax. What does this irreversibility mean? This, perhaps, that in the width of the physical prospects it opens up, the Phenomenon of Man may well be rivalled only by the inexorable physico-chemical drift towards the 'most probable' that we call entropy.

Hitherto science has been accustomed to construct the physical world solely from elements that are drawn, by the laws of chance and great numbers, towards an increasing dissipation of interchangeable energies and a state of inorganic diffusion. Once we have decided to see in mankind a physical phenomenon, we are obliged to conceive another fundamental irreversibility running counter to or across this first universal current. This is the irreversibility that leads things, in the op-

THE PHENOMENON OF MAN

posite direction from the probable, towards ever more improbable and more fully organic constructions. Side by side with
the measurable current of entropy, or running across it, there
is another current, impatient of measurement; it is disguised
in the material, comes to the surface of the organic, but is
most clearly visible in the human. This is the imponderable
current of Spirit.

I do not propose to consider here the problem of finding out
to what extent each of these currents may be reduced to a
function of the other within a third and more general movement.[2] It still remains true that if mankind does indeed represent their mutual reaction, the majesty of the Phenomenon
of Man and what makes it incomparably moving to us would
consist in its revealing to us, and making us experience from
within, at least one of these two primary impulses that carry
the world with them. It would be the universe, in one of its
fundamental movements, that would emerge in our consciousness, and the universe battling deep down in our wills.

Two important corollaries would derive from this situation,
were it accepted as a fact by science: the first somewhat speculative, the second eminently practical.

Speculatively, we would hold the key (allowing for the necessary analogies) that would allow us to explore from within the
universe that physics has, until now, tried to apprehend from
without. If it is indeed true, as we have seen, that the laws of
inorganic matter and the external processes of living matter
can continue upwards as far as us, and reappear 'hominised'
in us, it is because we can, conversely, try to understand them
both by making our way towards them from within, there to
meet ourselves again, materialised. In the domain of life, for

[2] Or whether, for example, the world of entropy instead of being the fundamental world that the physicists believe it to be, is more the material aspect
assumed, as a statistical effect of large numbers, by countless elementary spon-
taneities (in which case the universe would rest basically not upon mechanisms
but on 'liberties').

example, Édouard Le Roy[3] has recently shown how useful the concept of invention can be in shedding light on the mechanism of organic evolution.

Practically, we shall find ourselves the responsible trustees of a portion of universal energy that must be conserved and extended—not an indiscriminate energy, but one that has been brought, in us, to a supreme degree of elaboration. However coldly and objectively we may study things, we must still conclude that mankind constitutes a front along which the cosmos advances.

This would in the first place entail for us a new and noble obligation to make all the forces provided by the earth serve to advance the progress of the improbable. However, to harness material energies would still be only a secondary task. If the current of Spirit, represented today by mankind, is to continue to flow and to drive ahead, our chief concern would have to be to ensure that the human mass retains its *internal tension*: in other words, it must not allow the respect, the zest, the ardour for life, to run to waste in itself, nor to grow less. If that ardour cools, then what we have called the noosphere immediately withers away and disappears. In this we can get a hint of a new energetics (the maintenance, canalisation and magnification of human aspirations and passions) in which physics, biology and moral science would all be combined—a surprising combination, indeed, but one that is inevitable as soon as the reality of the Phenomenon of Man has been understood.

I need hardly say that these reflexions, which I hope may hasten the time when science will resolutely integrate mankind with the earth and the world, are provisional and no more than a beginning. At the same time it is difficult not to accept these two predictions:

1. If physics is ever to be the scientific cosmogony it hopes to

[3] *L'exigence idéaliste et le fait de l'Évolution* (Paris, 1927-8).

96

be, it will become progressively more impossible for it to confine itself to the study, from outside, of the phenomena governed by the laws of great numbers and subject to entropy. It will have to have recourse to complex symbols or functions in which the second aspect and the second current of things can be expressed: by those I mean the individual spontaneity and progressive organicity of the elements, seen from within. For all that they are impatient of measurement or calculation, these latter are no less physical than the phenomena which physics already studies.

2. After having been regarded for many years as a scientifically subsidiary or anomalous element of the universe, mankind will in the end be recognised as a fundamental phenomenon—*the* supreme phenomenon of Nature: that in which, in a unique complexity of material and moral factors, one of the principal acts of universal evolution is not only experienced but lived by us.

Paris, September, 1928

CHAPTER VI

CHRISTIANITY IN THE WORLD

---

1. Religion and mankind

The idea came to be widely accepted during the nineteenth century that religions express a primitive state of mankind that has now been left behind. 'In former times men developed the concept of divinity in their imaginations in order to account for natural phenomena of whose causes they were ignorant. By discovering the empirical explanation of these same phenomena, science has made God and religions superfluous.' That sums up the new creed of many of our contemporaries.

It is of the utmost importance to react against this narrow way of understanding the origin and the history of the idea of God in the world. There can be no doubt that the old forms assumed by religious sentiment were, to a great extent, confused. For a long time religion permeated, with no distinction of plane, a complex psychological mass from which there have in turn emerged experimental science, history, civic life, and so on, all with their own special methods and results. But this is a long way from meaning that the need for the absolute (on which all religions are based) disappeared in the course of that differentiation. As we shall see, we have only to look at the world of today, and more particularly the crisis it is now going through, with an impartial mind (we might even say a positivist mind) to be convinced of the contrary. Like a bud from which the scales have fallen, the religious nucleus in which all that is best in the life-sap of man is concentrated, can be seen at this very moment emerging more distinct and vigorous than ever.

If we are to understand the origin, development and present state of the religious question, we must, at least provisionally, ignore all secondary considerations of methods of worship and interpretation, and look squarely at the biological revolution produced in the terrestrial world by the appearance of man, that is, of thought. Before man, the whole of vital energy was almost entirely absorbed at every moment by the work of obtaining food, of reproduction, and of morphological evolution: the animals, like over-worked labourers, had not a moment's respite from their immediate task. They had neither the time nor the interior power to raise their heads and reflect. In man, on the contrary (as though the drill had suddenly struck oil) an overflow of power suddenly gushed to the surface. Because of his psychological organisation, man constantly (both in the space he covers and the time he foresees) exceeds the work required by his animality. Through man, an ocean of free energy (an energy as real and as 'cosmic' as the others with which physics is concerned) sets out to cover the earth. Through its higher manifestation, life emerges into the indeterminate and is in danger of getting out of gear. To counteract this, it is quite obvious that some appropriate system of co-ordination and control must be developed. Morality, which is too often regarded as a purely artificial organism (infra- or para-physical), is in fact simply the more or less rudimentary expression of the energetics of thought. The function, then, of religion, which is so often contemptuously relegated to metaphysics, is precisely in its turn to provide a foundation for morality, by introducing a dominating principle of order, and an axis of movement, into the restless and undisciplined multitude of reflective atoms: something of supreme value, to create, to hold in awe, or to love.

Religion, therefore, was not developed primarily as an easy

way out, to provide shelter from the insoluble or intrusive difficulties met by the mind as it became active. In its real basis, it is biologically (we might almost say mechanically) the necessary counterpart to the release of the earth's spiritual energy: the human being, by his appearance in nature, brings with him the emergence, ahead of him, of a divine pole to give him balance, just as necessarily as, in the particulate world explored by physics, the positive and negative elements of matter are linked together.

If that is so, the phenomenon of religion cannot be regarded as the manifestation of a transitory state, which is destined to grow weaker and disappear with the growth of mankind. The release of energy effected in the terrestial system by the establishment of the human zoological type constantly increases with the passage of time, so giving us a definition of and a standard of measurement for whatever reality is hidden under the word 'progress'. Through his social organisation, which apportions and divides the common task, man constantly increases the proportion of independence and leisure available to every citizen. By the introduction of machinery he suddenly increased this superabundance to a formidable degree. The whole human economy (once it fully understands its 'planetary' role) can have no other goal than constantly to enlarge on earth the excess of the psychic over matter. And that can mean only one thing: that religion, born to animate and control this overflow of spirit, must itself grow greater and more clearly defined in step with it and in the same degree. As soon as there is a gap between the release of conscious energy and the intensification of the sense of religion, then disorder is introduced; and it is all the more dangerous in that man is more adult. Is it not precisely this that we are now witnessing?

2. In search of a goal for life

Lack of employment. This phrase defines, in its most immediately apparent and most tangible aspect, the crisis the world is passing through at this moment: but at the same time it expresses the underlying cause of the evil that distresses us. Mankind began to be without occupation (at least potentially) from the first moment when its new-born mind was released from perception and immediate action, to wander in the domain of things that are distant or possible. But it did not have a profound sense of being without occupation (in fact, but even more in logic) so long as a predominant part of itself was still enslaved to a task that absorbed the greater part of its capacity for work. There are many symptoms to indicate that it is now without occupation, and that it may well continue to become increasingly so, now that the balance has finally been upset between material needs and powers of production, so that, in theory, all men have to do is to allow the machine that emancipated them to run on, and fold their arms. The present crisis is much more than a difficult interval accidentally encountered by a particular type of civilisation. Under contingent and local appearances, it expresses the inevitable result of the loss of equilibrium brought about in animal life by the appearance of thought. Men no longer know today how to occupy their physical powers: but what is more serious, they do not know towards what universal and final end they should direct the driving force of their souls. It has already been said, though without sufficiently deep appreciation of the words: the present crisis is a spiritual crisis. Material energy is no longer circulating with sufficient freedom because it is not finding a spirit strong enough to organise and lead its mass; and the spirit is not strong enough because it is continually being dissipated in restless, undisciplined, activity. We may transpose those terms by applying the observations

101

made in the preceding paragraph: mankind today is undecided, and distressed, at the very peak of its power, because it
has not defined its spiritual pole. It lacks religion.

Let us analyse this lack in more detail and see if we can disclose the features of the Messiah for whom we are waiting. The
'religious function', we were saying earlier, grows in the same
direction and at the same speed, as 'hominisation'; but at the
same time it takes on a new, and more closely determined,
form with each new phase of mankind. What, then, are the
conditions that must be fulfilled by the particular religion that
can save us, if it is to carry out its biological role as animator?

These conditions may be deduced very simply from the
consideration of a psychological phenomenon which, much
more, I am sure, than the astonishing material transforma-
tions we are witnessing, will be recognised by historians of the
future as characteristic of our age. In the space of a century the
combined influence of history, physics, philosophy and sociology, has shown us that the whole universe is carried along in
an over-all movement (or evolution) within which the special
evolution of consciousness has its determined place. Time
now appears to us not as the permanent setting of divergent
or circular diversifications but as the axis of a sort of cosmogenesis. Things do not repeat themselves, but the world presses
on.

These evolutionary views have entered much more deeply
into our psychology than is commonly believed, and under
their influence a particular type of religious requirement has
asserted itself in mankind. Both because of our intellectual
apprehension of Nature in movement and because of our
corresponding appetite for action, we can no longer accept
any control of our activity *that is not directed to the fulfilment
of a world that includes us integrally in its consummation.* The
free, thinking, energy released by the earth can no longer
be dominated *by the ideal of any established order that has to be*

accepted and preserved. Morality and religion (like the entire social order) *have ceased to be for us a static: if they are to appeal to us, and save us, they must be a dynamic.*

'We no longer want a religion of regulation: but we dream of a religion of conquest.' In saying that, we have, without realising it, taken a great step towards belief, cutting across and rising above our modern lack of faith. It has become a commonplace to designate western civilisation as materialist —the civilisation which is the focus point of the new mankind. Nothing could be more unjust. The West has overthrown many idols. But, by its discovery of the *dimensions and forward momentum of the universe*, it has set in motion a powerful mysticism. For we can properly speak of it as a mysticism, in that we have been aroused by physics and history to the consciousness of a tangible immensity, and so can conceive no values, can take delight in nothing, except our arduous identification with the fulfilment of that immensity. The whole problem now is to determine the truth and the name of the presence that we believe we can feel behind the blaze of the universe.—If our feeling is no more than a dream (if, that is, there is nothing final and permanent at the end of our efforts) then goodbye, once and for all, to the fine torch held aloft by man. The 'free energy' of the earth can find no valid use for its enthusiasm. Mankind will have lived just long enough to be certain that it lacked the one thing in the world that made life worth living. This, it would seem, is a hypothesis that must be ruled out, for it would reduce the universe to an absurdity. But if, on the other hand, there is in truth at the other end of cosmic duration Some Thing or Some One towards whom we are advancing, then we must contrive to know his nature better, so that we may the better worship him.

3. Religions put to the test

The biological function of religion is to give a form to the free psychic energy of the world. And the only form that the development of mankind can accept is that of a process of construction and conquest that leads up to some supreme unification of the universe.

If we apply this double criterion to the numerous types of religious, and even secular moral systems, that have followed one another *uninterruptedly* throughout history, they all go up in smoke. Just as practically nothing survives factually beyond its own time, so practically nothing can stand up logically.

The first to be eliminated, at one sweep, are the various forms of agnosticism, explicit or implicit, that have tried to base morality on a pure social empiricism or again on a pure individual aestheticism, emphatically ruling out any faith in some future consummation of the world. Apart from the individual shortcomings of these various systems, they all have the common fault of cutting off the flow of the life-sap which they should direct into the proper channel and help to rise. Neither Confucianism, which ensured the smooth running of society without progress—nor the wisdom of Marcus Aurelius, whose thought was a bright flower in the garden of mankind—nor the cult, so popular again today, of *self-contained* personal enjoyment and interior perfection—none of these can any longer come up in any way to our ideal of men as builders and conquerors. It is upon a heaven that we must be urged to launch our attack: *if not, we lay down our arms.*

If we turn to the group represented by Islam, nothing has permanence; everything evaporates, and perhaps even more completely. Islam has retained the idea of the existence and the greatness of God. That, it is true, is the seed from which everything may one day be born again; but at the same time Islam has achieved the extraordinary feat of making this God as ineffective and sterile as a non-being for all that concerns the knowledge and betterment of the world. After destroying a great deal and creating locally an ephemeral beauty, Islam offers itself today as a principle of fixation and stagnation. An improvement upon this practical impotence would be perfectly conceivable, and—*basically amounting to a convergence towards Christianity* (see below)—already appears to be coming about in a group of high-minded thinkers alive to modern requirements. Until that renascence comes about, the Allah of the Koran will remain a God for the Bedouin. He could never attract the effort of any truly civilised man.

Next we turn to the imposing mass of Hindu and eastern mystical systems. The East, the first shrine, and, we are assured, the ever-living dwelling place of the Spirit. The East, where so many from the West still dream of finding shelter for their faith in life ... Let us take a closer look at those mighty constructions; and, without even venturing into the temple to savour what sort of incense still burns within it, let us, not as archaeologists or poets, but as architects of the future, examine the solidity of its walls. The very moment we come into fundamental contact with Asia there can be no question of doubt. Those impressive columns are utterly incapable of supporting the drive of our world in these days. The incomparable greatness of the religions of the East lies in their having been second to none in vibrating with the passion for unity. This note, which is essential to every form of mysticism, has even penetrated them so deeply that we find ourselves falling under a spell simply by uttering the names of their Gods. However, the Hindu sages thought that if man is to attain this unity he must renounce the earth, its passions and cares, and the effort it demands.

They held that the multiple within which we are struggling is the legacy of a bad dream. 'Dispel this illusion, this Maya, stifle every noise', they taught, 'and then you will wake in the essential void, where there is neither sound, nor shape, nor love.' It is, logically, a doctrine of passivity, of relaxation of tension, of withdrawal from things. A doctrine, in fact, that is totally ineffective and dead. It is precisely the *reverse* of what true human mysticism, born in the West, looks for if it is to be able to develop itself fully. For the western mystic the unity that demands our worship is to be found at the term not of a suppression or attenuation of the real but of an effort of universal convergence. God is arrived at not in a negation, but in an extension, of the world.

We must never allow ourselves to be run away with by the vast sophism of the East. We must follow straight along our own path, and so discover whether some other divinity than the Nirvana awaits us on the road of the West.

4. *The possibility of Christianity*

It is, in fact, only Christianity that still stands firm today, with the ability to come up to the measure of the intellectual and moral world that was born in the West with the Renaissance. It would appear that no one who has been deeply influenced by modern culture and the knowledge that goes with it can sincerely be a Confucian, a Buddhist or a Moslem (unless he is prepared to live a double interior life, or profoundly to modify for his own use the terms of his religion). On the other hand, such a man can claim to be and believe that he is completely Christian.

If we ask the reason for this difference, we shall find that it derives from one single fact: that Christianity, in spite of certain appearances, which both its friends and its enemies seem only too willing to emphasise, is in fact, the only one among all existing forms of belief which is *a religion of universal progress*. Like Buddhism, it is true, Christianity preaches detachment; it urges men to asceticism; at least in its origins, it peopled the deserts (as now it cultivates them); it has produced saints and a literature that are reminiscent of the life and teaching of the fakirs. In these various characteristics, it mirrors eastern religions, of which it may possibly retain certain influences or certain seeds that periodically shoot up again. But there is something deeper in Christianity than an admiration for the Stylites, or the anti-intellectualism of the *Imitation*—and that is its faith in the resurrection of the earth and the expectation of a consummation of the universe 'in Christ Jesus'. Now, *the living logic of this hope extends very far,* much further, even, than the official rulers of the Churches realise or would wish. If nothing 'of the breadth and length and height' of the world is to escape Christ, what the Christian has to do is not, like the Buddhist, to withdraw from things *by avoiding them*. He must *leave them behind* by exploring them, measuring them, conquering them as fully as possible. And this not for his own sake by any means, so that he can enjoy them; but entirely in order to extract from them and return to God all the essence of beauty and spirituality they contain. It is, once more, renunciation, but a renunciation that involves a 'traversing', a creative renunciation, in which the pain is simply the *sign* of the effort: it is not a renunciation by breaking away from things, by reducing contact with them, one in which the suffering is wrongly accorded an absolute value. For the authentic Christian the solution of the mystical problem is to be found at the opposite pole from the 'eastern' solution. The divine unity is attained by sublimation, not by negation, of the world. Its radiance shines from the peak of a purification which is a universal *convergence*. This, we have seen, is precisely the essential postulate of the modern mind, in other words of the religion that is *implicit in the western concept* of the developments of life. It is not in the least surprising, therefore, that the Christian—if he is sufficiently informed about his faith to have penetrated to the Spirit that underlies

107

the sometimes heavy disguise of the letter—feels himself in no way lost in the wide ocean of modern thought; there he can develop in complete intellectual and effective freedom, as though he were in his own native home. The Cross is not a shadow of death—but a symbol of progress. Christianity does not dispense the opium of a defeatist passivity, but the lucid intoxication of a magnificent reality *to be discovered by an advance along the whole front of the universe*. In spite of certain inevitable blunders, it has hitherto made us not *inhuman but superhuman*, and that is what it still seeks to do. We see, then, why, as a faith, it remains *acceptable* to a generation that requires a religion to do more than keep us good and bind up our wounds—it must fill us with the spirit of criticism, of enthusiasm, of enquiry, and of conquest.

That Christianity, however, should be acceptable and *possible*, still means nothing. Is it, as it claims, more than that, the *only possible* religion? Without a 'convergent' view of the world, of which the Christian type is an example, the structure built up by human effort is in danger of collapsing for lack of a keystone to set in the arch. So much we must admit. But in that case is there anything to prevent us from conceiving or expecting any number of other saviours of the same type as Christ? Why must we adhere to the Christian movement as though *it alone* were true?

The whole religious problem of the future is centred on that final question.

5. The religion of tomorrow

Fully to accept that Christianity is not only satisfying but true, is to believe not only that it directs our free activity in a direction that is biologically advantageous, but also that there is justification for its claim to bring us into relationship (anticipated or adumbrated) with the *actual* Centre of the world: and that, not in a symbolic but a trans-experiential way.

The classical apologists relied, to establish this prerogative, on miracles, whose appearance, if we are to believe them, was the 'specific' test appropriate to 'true' religion.

I would be most unwilling to deny the possibility, or indeed the likelihood, of the *true* religion being closely associated with an unexpected relaxation of determinisms, caused by some super-animation of Nature under the influence of a power radiating from God; nevertheless we have to recognise that, as a consideration, the miracle has ceased to have an effective impact on our minds. Its establishment involves such historical and physical difficulties that there are probably very many Christians who at the present moment are still believers not *because of* but *in spite of* the wonders related by Scripture.[1]

What has more influence on our minds is the consideration of the astonishing harmony that is constantly to be found, as time goes on, between the Christian God and the most subtle developments of our human ideal. In the sciences, it is a recognised proof of the 'reality' of an object (even one, like an atom, that cannot be directly observed) that it can be distinguished, always in the same form, by a series of different methods; this complete consistency possessed by something that remains identical in a varied group of experiments defines a 'natural nucleus' as certainly as does touch or sight. It is the same, it would seem, with Christ. Millions of lives (among the best of lives) have been spent for the last two thousand years, and are still engaged, in applying to this mysterious Object the most subtle and most searching tests known to our psychological experience. Countless minds and hearts have asked this Christ to satisfy their most imperative and finest

---

[1] According to St Thomas, the truth can be received (and hence transmitted) only according to the capacity of the receiver: Nihil recipitur in aliquo nisi secundum proportionem recipientis. (1 Sent. 8, 5, 3c.) Here the authority of theology supports reason: it is evident that the Gospel miracles could be recorded only in terms of the elementary knowledge of the time: hence the difficulty raised for contemporary thought by the account of some of those miracles. (Ed.)

aspirations. *And he has never been found lacking.* On the contrary, he has always emerged from this test (such that probably no other reality in the world has had to face its like) with a greater capacity to stimulate around him a more wonderfully synthetic effort of all our faculties: an astonishing object, indeed, which can be apprehended as an experiential element, sought after as an ideal, cherished as a person, worshipped as a world. *This endless capacity of harmonising with the whole physical and psychological order of our universe* can have but one explanation: the Christ who gradually reveals himself to Christian thought is not a phantasy nor a symbol (*if that were so he would be found in some way wanting or would cease to satisfy us*); he is, or at least he introduces, the reality of what, through the whole structure of human activity, we are awaiting.[2]

We can come to the same conclusion by following another road, which has the advantage of enabling us to take in those general analogies of the universe whose over-all harmony is often more effectively convincing than the restricted logic of any syllogism. The fact of religion, as we said earlier, is a biological phenomenon, directly associated with the increase in the release of the earth's psychic energy. *The curve it follows is therefore not individual, nor national, nor racial, but human.* Religion, like science or civilisation, has (if I may use the term) an 'ontogenesis' co-extensive with the history of mankind. Thus true religion (by which I mean the form of religion at which the general groping of reflective action on earth will one day arrive), like every other reality of the 'planetary' order, partakes of the nature of a 'phylum'. It must be possible to trace its origins back to the beginning of all time. That means that *at some particular moment* in human duration (and even more once the embryonic period had been left behind) a specially favoured current of religious thought must (as it still must) have represented in a relatively distinct form the living fibre

[2] Cf. Hebrews, ii. i: 'Faith is the assurance of things hoped for'. (Ed.)

of the faith in which the future will permanently develop. All the religious currents, therefore, are not at every moment on an equal footing—any more than in the past of the animal world all the phyla were destined to emerge into humanity. *On every page of the earth's history*, one of them (or at any rate one group of them) represents the place at which one must stand if one is to forward and experience more effectively the progress of the divinisation of the world. And we are no more free to alter this condition than we are to change the axes of a crystal or of a living body. If we apply this to our world today, we shall find, as we were saying earlier, that only one religious current can be seen at the present time which is capable of meeting the requirements and aspirations of modern thought; only one religion *is both possible and phyletic*: Christianity. There can be no shadow of a doubt. It is through Christianity that there runs the fibre which we are looking for, knowing that the fibre must exist. If Christianity is now the only factually possible religion, it is because it is the only one logically possible. The divine, with which mankind cannot do without if it is not to fall back into dust, will be found for us only if we adhere closely to the movement from which Christ is progressively emerging.

How, then, are we to envisage the coming developments of faith on earth?

In the form, we may be sure, of a slow concentration of man's power of worship around a Christianity that has gradually reached the stage of being '*religion for the sake of research and effort*'. The first great event to come about (and it is undoubtedly already happening) will be the schism between those who believe and those who do not believe in the future of the world: the non-believers, logically lost to every creed (which will have become to them without purpose or goal) and to every conquest (now without interest or value); the believers, biologically impelled to adhere to the only religious organism in which faith in the world retains the two characteristics that are proper to real things: indefinite coherence with facts, and co-extension with duration. The world must be converted in its whole mass, or it will, by physiological necessity, fall into decay. And, if it is converted, it will be by convergence around a *religion of action* that will gradually be seen to be identical with, and governed by, *Christianity faithfully extended to its utmost limit.*

From this a final conclusion can be drawn: Christianity does not represent in the world, as would sometimes appear, simply the religious side of a transient civilisation that flowered in the West. It is much more, like the Western ethos itself (whose mysticism it expresses and whose hopes it justifies) a phenomenon of universal embrace, which marks the appearance within the human stratum of a new vital order.

Peking, May 1933

CHAPTER VII

MODERN UNBELIEF

La Vie Intellectuelle has done me the honour of including me in its inquiry into the present causes of unbelief. I am all the more willing to answer in that, having been living for the last twenty years in contact with and in sympathy with unbelieving circles, I have only to look at my memories to attempt a solution of the problem we are presented with. I shall quote no name or book; but I believe that the objectivity of my evidence may be relied upon.

That evidence will not take long.

To my mind, the primary source of modern unbelief (which is so wide-spread that in many intellectual fields believers are an exception) is to be found in the unwarranted schism that since the Renaissance has gradually cut off Christianity from what one might call the *natural human religious current*. The modern world, as I understand it, is not radically unbelieving or non-religious. But its natural capacity for worship is now diverted to an object, the universe, which *seems* to it to be in opposition to the Christian God. Hence the evil, and hence, too, the remedy.

Let me explain.

1. *The evil*

In an ill-defined way ever since the Renaissance but most distinctly for almost the last hundred and fifty years, a great change (a revolution, one might say) has been effected in the deepest reaches of the human mind. Through all the channels

113

of experience and thought, we have become conscious of the unitary greatness of the cosmos and the organic significance of time. In a century and a half, the laws of birth and growth that we used to recognise for certain beings and for certain limited domains have been generally extended to the dimensions of the universe. Henceforth we shall never cease to realise that the world has a past and a future, which means that it has a growth. As we look around us and into ourselves, we can see that the universe is not merely a large static association made up of fully formed objects, but a specific whole, with a power of organic development.

From the scientific and philosophical point of view, this way of looking at the universe has consequences of obvious importance: its influence is necessarily felt, and felt effectively (though this has not yet been sufficiently emphasised) even in the religious depths of the soul. By taking on a sort of natural unity in the course of duration, the world does more than acquire an additional dimension in the eyes of intellectual inquiry. It stands out, in its encounter with the human individual, as an object endowed with higher value and dignity, to which it is clear, he must subordinate and dedicate himself. It arouses in us, with the undeniable appeal of a tangible immensity close to us, the resonance of the chords, ever ready to vibrate, of worship.

It is well worth taking the trouble to observe the fact without being side-tracked by the polymorphous appearance of the new faith, and the infantile way in which it is often expressed. In a few generations, mankind has been literally and spontaneously *converted* to a sort of religion of the world—ill-defined in its dogmas but perfectly clear in its moral orientations. These are: the recognition of the primacy of the whole over the individual; a passionate faith in the value and potentialities of human effort; an extremely vivid appreciation of the sacred character of research *in all the lines it follows*. As a

114

result of the scientific discovery of the natural unity of the world and its vastness, modern man can now recognise God only in the continuation (could one, perhaps, say 'under the species?') of some universal progress or maturing.

How, then, does modern man see the Christian God?

To those who are not *extremely familiar* with it, Christianity *quite certainly* gives the impression of having escaped, and even to be resisting, the psychological 'revolution' we have just been analysing. It is not making up its mind frankly to accept, in their general application and *their spirit*, the views on cosmic development that are universally accepted everywhere except in Christianity. It seems to delight in belittling human hopes and pointing out the weaknesses of our society. It despises or fears progress and discovery; in short, it in no way hallows or magnifies the loftiest and most intensely felt aspirations of modern man. That is the *outward impression* it gives: we, who are inside Christianity, know that it is deceptive; but it is nevertheless a terrible disappointment for those who see us from outside.

In their search for a name to give to the unknown God whose existence they dimly apprehend, the Gentiles look to us. And then they turn away from a gospel that seems to be alien to their outlook on the world and to meet neither their questions nor their expectations. The resistance the Church now encounters in becoming accepted does not arise, as is sometimes said, from its dogmas being too lofty or its moral teaching too difficult. It is due to the fact that men, no longer recognising in us their religious and moral ideal, are turning away from us and looking for *something better*.

2. The Remedy

If the above analysis is accurate, if, that is, modern unbelief is indeed caused by a sort of 'occultation' of the 'revealed-God' by the 'world-God', then the *direct* means of curing the evil from which we are suffering is immediately apparent. What we have to do is to make it clear that the universe, as it now presents itself to our investigations, is far from eclipsing the Christian God: it is simply waiting to be transfigured by him and receive him as its crown. If we want men to return to God, carried to him by the very current that seems to be driving them away, we must ourselves open wide our minds and hearts to the new outlook and aspirations—that so we may first make them our own, and then Christianise them.

First, to make them our own: and here we must examine our consciences. Have not we who are Christians remained, if the truth is told, too alien to the spirit of the mankind it is our duty to save? In spite of the Church's remonstrances, has not what is in practice a sort of Baianism[1] crept into our way of judging the effects on the world of the Fall? Have we not allowed (I quote) 'the notions of sin and individual salvation to become hypertrophied in our religion'? Do we not too often spread around us not the light of the Cross but its shadow?

We may be sure that everything is not evil in the wind of victorious optimism that is rousing the mass of mankind. Why should we shelter from it? Is not the gospel a leaven that we have to introduce into the heart of the world? '*Non veni solvere, sed adimplere.*'

To consummate is to Christianise. And if we are to effect that transformation, we shall need more, we feel, than a purely intellectual or negative criticism that destroys the false forms of materialism and pantheism. Our mission is to assume (*induere*) the religious spirit of the modern world, in its natural fulness, and to live it, fully and sincerely, *on the Christian plane*. The religious aspirations of modern humanita-

[1] The reference is to the exaggerated Augustinianism condemned in the teaching of the Flemish theologian Michael Baius (1513–89). (Tr.)

rianism are distressingly vague and aimless. It is for us to show, *verbo et exemplo*, that only the concrete reality of Christ is at hand to strengthen them, give them a central focus, and bring them to salvation. When Christians, in virtue of their very Christianity, through the constructive activity of their charity, through their renunciation—positive and fruitful—through the confident boldness of their supernatural views—when they show themselves to be the first of men to spiritualise earthly values and press forward into the future—then the better, which means the most dangerous, part of human unbelief will be disarmed, its very soul left defenceless.

One single proposition can sum up all that is essential in our answer to the question raised by *La Vie Intellectuelle*:

The world is being converted spontaneously to a sort of natural religion of the universe, which is wrongly turning it away from the God of the gospel: it is in this that its 'unbelief' consists. We must convert that conversion itself, taking it one step further, by showing, through our whole lives, that only Christ, *in quo omnia constant*, is capable of animating and guiding the newly sensed progress of the universe: and, from the very extension of what is producing today's unbelief, there will perhaps emerge the faith of tomorrow.

Answer to a questionnaire:
from 'La Vie Intellectuelle', 25 October 1933

CHAPTER VIII

SOME REFLEXIONS ON THE CONVERSION OF THE WORLD[1]

---

1. The present form assumed by the problem of the conversion of the world: the nascent world

At the present moment Christianity is faced by a completely new situation. In its origins, its role was to conquer and transform a world *that was coming to an end*. Later it had the relatively easy task of organising the world of European civilisation to which it had given birth. Now (and, to put it briefly, ever since the Renaissance) a new form of human growth can be seen, which has appeared within the Church but not under her aegis. After the greco-roman world and the medieval world, a third world, the modern world, is emerging; it is developing as marginal to Christianity, and with a human potential much stronger than that possessed by the latter: the whole impulse and all the initiative of the earth in recent times, derive, we must admit, from 'the modern spirit'.

There is no question now of heresies or schisms or even of paganism. The pagans, in the traditional meaning of the word, were or still are, mere 'survivals'. What we are now faced with is a *nascent* human current.

It is a new situation and calls for a new method of attack and conversion.

---

[1] This report was asked for by a member of the Apostolic Delegation in China, who wished to pass it on to a high official in Rome: the original, accordingly, has a note 'for the use of a prince of the Church'.

2. The apparently anti-Christian character of the nascent world: the conflict between the two religions

If we are completely to understand the problem and find its solution, we must carry further our analysis of the nascent world: considering it, I need hardly add, in its living and progressive part, which is the only part that can compete with the Church.

In theory, it should have been possible for this world to come into being and grow as a believing world. What is the reason for its emancipation, and why does the child try to strike out at its mother and cut itself off from her?

I see the reason for this antagonism between Christianity and Modernism in the two essential discoveries from which the modern spirit arose and whose influence still runs through it.

a. First, the discovery of the structurally linked immensity of Space, which introduces a note of *universalism* into our customary outlook on things.

b. Secondly, the discovery of the structurally linked (and progressively increasing) immensity of *duration*, which again introduces into our customary outlook the note of limitless potential progress (futurism).

Universalism and futurism, combining in the perception of a universe which is in process of global growth (evolution). In themselves, these two characteristics constitute by their appearance a great psychological event, since they amount to the acquisition by our experience of two new dimensions. But they do more: by their nature, they define a *religion*, since the 'religious' appears, by definition, as soon as the world is seen in its totality and in its consummation in the future ('faith').

This nascent religion (and this is the cardinal point) does not, at first sight, appear to harmonise with Christianity: not that the latter is not itself, too, essentially 'universalist and futurist', but because those two words are understood by each party in a seemingly different sense. Because of their origin, the universalism and futurism of the world are pantheist in tendency, immanent, organicist, evolutionary; while those of Christianity are expressed primarily in terms of personality, transcendence, juridical relationships, and immutability.

There you have the essence of the present conflict. The true struggle we are witnessing is not between believers and non-believers, but between two sorts of believers. Two ideals, two conceptions of the Divine, are confronting one another. The best (and that means the most dangerous) anti-Christians do not reject Christianity because it is too difficult, but because it does not seem fine enough to them. If they do not accept Christ, it is because they do not recognise in him the characteristics of what they worship and look for. A religion of the earth is being mobilised against the religion of heaven. That is the basic situation, in all its gravity but also in the hopes it contains.

3. General method of solving the conflict: not condemnation but baptism

Faced by this conflict between the Christian faith and the modern, what must we do to save the world?

a. A first solution would be to reject, condemn and (if possible) suppress the new religion as a devilish proliferation. This method has in fact been tried, but with results that were bound to be positively bad. Not only is it an impossible undertaking to try to halt the modern movement (since it is involved in the very development of human consciousness), but there is something unjust and anti-Christian in the attempt. Whatever grounds there may be for condemning many of the forms taken by 'faith in the world', they proceed from an undeniable effort to be true to life (in other words, to the creative action of God), and that effort must be respected. In fact the movement that represents nothing less than a transformation effected in the *anima naturaliter religiosa* of the whole human race, has already found its way, as was inevitable, into Christianity itself. Christians, as a result of a change that is inherent in the human mass of which they form a part, can no longer worship precisely as they used to do (before the appearance of Space and Time). That explains the unspoken dissatisfaction of so many of the faithful with a Christianity that tells them to beware of views and hopes that they cannot help sharing. It is the source, too, of their anxieties about a faith that believes itself to be threatened by all the refocusing and enlargement of outlook on the universe that man is now effecting. Many Christians are beginning to feel that the image of God they are being offered is not worthy of the universe we know.

b. Another solution, accordingly, suggests itself to our minds as more satisfactory and effective than 'condemnation'. This would be to proceed as follows: to realise and demonstrate that in its essence the modern 'religion of the earth' is simply an unconscious impulse towards heaven—so that the energies that seem to present such a threat to the Church are on the contrary a new contribution, with the power to bring new life to the ancient Christian stock. Not to condemn, but to baptise and assimilate. It is clear that the nascent world (which is the only one that matters) would be converted practically at one stroke, if it were recognised that the divinity it worships is precisely the Christian God comprehended at a deeper level. Is this conjunction of the two divine stars possible? I believe it is, and that it can be effected in the following stages.

121

4. A synthesis of the new and the old: the universal Christ

If we wish to get to the bottom of the modern religious current, and reverse it, three linked steps seem to me to be necessary:

a. The first step would consist in developing (on the lines of the 'Philosophia perennis': primacy of being, act and potency) a correct physics and metaphysics of evolution. I am convinced that a loyal interpretation of the new conclusions of science and thought leads legitimately not to a materialistic evolutionism but to an evolutionism in terms of spirit. The world we know does not develop haphazardly, but is structurally dominated by a *Personal Centre* of universal convergence.

b. The second step is dogmatic. It would consist in formulating a Christology proportionate to the dimensions now attributed to the universe—that means, in recognising that in virtue of the mechanism of the Incarnation, Christ possesses 'universal' or 'cosmic' attributes in addition to his strictly human and divine attributes (with which theologians have hitherto been primarily concerned): and it is precisely those attributes that make him the personal Centre which the physics and metaphysics of evolution feel must exist and for which they are looking. These views show a startling coincidence with the most fundamental Johannine and Pauline texts and with the theology of the Greek Fathers.

c. A third step, mystical and moral, would then be taken automatically, and would consist in developing a gospel of human conquest. It is indeed impossible for Christ to be seen more plainly as the peak of universal evolution, without Christians disclosing more clearly the supernatural value of human effort in Christo Jesu. For some time it might have seemed that the most direct road to heaven was that which most quickly left the earth behind. Now the universal Christ is at hand to make us understand that heaven can be attained only through the completion of the earth and the world—which are both now much larger and more unfinished than we used to think; and with that understanding the fundamental Christian attitude, without any distortion, is enriched and 'energised'.

The Cross is now not only the symbol of expiation, but the token, too, of growth through suffering.

Detachment does not consist, properly speaking, in contemning and rejecting, but in penetrating and sublimating.[2]

Resignation is simply the final form of the struggle against evil—the transformation, in God, of inevitable defeats.

Charity does more than call on us to bind up wounds: it urges us to build a better world here below, and to be in the forefront of every attack launched to forward the growth of mankind. 'Plus et ego . . .'

And personal salvation is important not so much because it will bring about our own beatification as because it makes us effect in ourselves the salvation of the world.

Thus, in the threefold sphere of philosophical thought, of dogma, and of moral teaching, there would be developed a Christianity that is given new youth by the revelation of the universal Christ. Now, it is evident:

1. That such a religion is exactly in line with what the modern world is looking for as its God, and regards as its specific form of worship: a God who justifies, sets the crown upon, and receives as a supreme tribute, the incessant ('adhuc parturit') labour of the consummation, even on earth, of man.

2. Nevertheless, it is also clear that this same religion in no way represents a compromise between Christianity and the modern world. In taking on universality, Christ is not lost in the heart of the universe (as he was in those forms of modernism that were condemned): he dominates and assimilates the universe by imposing upon it the three essential charac-

[2] In other words, privation ceases to be synonymous with perfection.

teristics of his traditional truth—the *personal* nature of the Divine; the manifestation of this supreme Personality in the *historical Christ*; the *super-terrestrial* nature of the world consummated in God. The 'universalised' Christ takes over, correcting and completing them, the energies that undoubtedly lie hidden in modern forms of pantheism. He grows greater by remaining what he was—or, to put it more exactly, *in order to* remain what he was.

In fact, the more one thinks about it, the clearer it becomes that to 'universalise' Christ is the only way we have of retaining in him his essential attributes (alpha and omega) in a fantastically enlarged Creation. If Christianity is to keep its place at the head of mankind, it must make itself explicitly recognisable as a sort of 'pan-Christism'—which, in fact, is simply the notion of the mystical Body, taken in its fullest and most profound sense, and the extension to the universe of the attributes already accorded (particularly with reference to human society) to Christ the King.

5. A possible new era for Christianity: interior liberation and expansion

By making plain the splendours of the universal Christ, Christianity, without ceasing to be for the earth the water that purifies and the oil that soothes, acquires a new value. By the very fact that it provides the earth's aspirations with a goal that is at once *immense, concrete* and *assured*, it rescues the earth from the disorder, the uncertainties, and the nausea that are the most terrible of tomorrow's dangers. It provides the fire that inspires man's effort. In other words, it is seen to be the form of faith that is most fitted to modern needs: a religion for progress—the very religion of progress of the earth—I would go so far as to say the very religion of evolution.

I am convinced that an Epiphany of this sort would be for Christianity the signal for a vast movement of interior liberation and expansion.

a. Interior liberation. As we were saying earlier, numbers of Christians feel stifled and humiliated in a faith that often seems to make it its business to question and damp their enthusiasm for a rebuilding of the earth. What a blessed sense of release there would be in the Church, if in the name of this same faith—now a stimulus instead of being only a brake—they could feel themselves engaged in the total conquest of the world, for the universal supremacy of Christ!

b. And what a revelation, to those outside the Church, of the might of Christianity! It is abundantly clear that Christianity is no longer advancing as rapidly as it should. In spite of the fact that the work of the propagation of the faith has never been organised with such vigour, we may well wonder whether the world as a whole, in all the best of its representatives and in its vital forces, is coming closer to Christ or whether it is in fact drifting further away. As I see it, this situation arises from a perfectly clear cause: 'Christianity, in the form we preach it, lacks sufficient contagious power.' We are no longer understood. How often have I heard it said, in complete sincerity, by non-believers, 'If I became a Christian, I would feel that I was less a man', or again, 'We so badly need another revelation.' Christ offering himself as the salvation, not only of the 'supernatural' soul, but also of the whole physical structure that conditions souls—Christ manifesting himself, not hidden in clouds, but clothed in the energies of the world in which he is immersed ('Christus amictus mundo')—Christ, no longer the condemner but the Saviour of the modern world and its hopes in the future—such a Christ would immediately draw to himself all the vital part of mankind.

His love would spread in the only way that befits the true religion: like fire.

In order to convert the world, we Christians must produce many more missionaries; but above all we must, *with all that is human in us*, re-think our religion.

6. *A decisive step: Christian optimism*

'With all that is human in us'—I used those words deliberately, in order to emphasise what at this moment seems to me to be essential if we are to turn towards Christianity the undecided energies that are emerging in our world: *Christianity must at last accept unreservedly the new dimensions (spatial, temporal and psychological) of the world around us.*

I am not blind, of course, to the many steps the Church has taken in recent years to reconcile itself to the modern world. But reconciliation is not acceptance. Behind the particular concessions that Christianity has made, there is a fear (I am speaking primarily of the Gentiles) that one can still detect the same fundamental opposition, or, if not opposition, distrust: as though the Church were unwilling to become committed, to surrender itself: as though, running more deeply than encouraging gestures in matters of detail, the same thought was lurking in the back of its mind: 'Fundamentally, there is, and there never will be, anything new under the sun. Nothing can change the face of the earth. Was not the earth, in any case, weighed down and warped by the Fall?' Still the talk goes on of the 'mundus senescens'—'the ageing world'—the 'mundus frigescens'—'the world growing cold'—never of the 'mundus nascens'—'the nascent world'. In brief, while the Church verbally accepts certain results and certain prospects of progress, she seems 'not to believe in them'. Sometimes she gives her blessing but her heart does not go with it.

The consequences of this sceptical (or even pessimistic) attitude towards man are such as completely to paralyse the progress of the conversion of the world.

On the one hand, non-believers outside the Church continue to regard us as insincere. They either shun us, or hate us, because we do not share their sufferings, their work, or their hopes.

On the other hand, the faithful inside the Church continue to feel ill at ease, caught as they are between their faith and their natural convictions or aspirations. Thus they lack the strength to assimilate the human forces all around them.

You can convert only what you love: if the Christian is not fully in sympathy with the nascent world—if he does not *experience* in himself the anxieties and aspirations of the modern world—if he does not allow the sense of man to grow greater in his being—then he will never effect the emancipating synthesis between earth and heaven from which can emerge the parousia of the universal Christ. He will continue to fear and condemn almost indiscriminately everything that is new, without seeing among the blemishes and evils the hallowed efforts of something that is being born.

To plunge into in order then to emerge and raise up. To share in order to sublimate. That is precisely the law of the Incarnation. One day, already a thousand years ago, the Popes bade farewell to the world of Rome and decided to 'go over to the barbarians'. Is it not just such a gesture, but even more fundamental, that the present day looks for?

I believe that the world will never be converted to Christianity's hopes of heaven, unless first Christianity is converted (that so it may divinise them) to the hopes of the earth.

Peking, 9 October 1936

CHAPTER IX

THE SALVATION OF MANKIND

THOUGHTS ON THE PRESENT CRISIS

Far from growing less acute, the crisis inaugurated by the Great War is becoming more extensive and more profound, to such a degree that we are beginning to realise its true nature. Beginning as no more than a conflict between material interests, it is now making itself felt in fundamental upheavals within the mass of humanity. Three currents today, or to speak more precisely, four, are beating against us and sweeping us off our feet. In the centre, democracy, already ageing, which less than fifty years ago seemed permanently to have conquered the world. To left and right, youthful communism and youthful fascism, both in full growth. And finally, above all three (or so, at least, it used to believe) but amazed at the repercussions of the struggle it feels even in its own soul, stands Christianity.[1]

For the last twenty years we have been trying to retain our hope that our troubles were simply the last manifestations of a storm that had blown itself out. Everything would soon calm down, and life, we thought, would certainly in the end continue again as before.

We now have to accept it as proven that mankind has just entered into what is probably the most extensive period of transformation it has known since its birth. The seat of the evil we are suffering from is to be found in the very foundations of thought on earth. Something is happening in the

[1] Père Teilhard, it will be appreciated, was describing the situation at the time of writing, November 1936. (Ed.)

general structure of Spirit: it is a new type of life that is beginning.

Faced by, or rather reeling under the impact of such an upheaval, no man can remain indifferent. The concern and anxiety aroused by this vast phenomenon that is taking place are penetrating even into the calm atmosphere of the laboratory. And those of us, accordingly (geologists, palaeontologists, prehistorians), who are professionally used to embracing vast expanses of duration and to distinguishing far-reaching over-all movements, are instinctively trying to weigh up what is happening in the life of our world and to foresee where these events are taking us. What is taking place biologically in the human stratum, where is it all leading us, and how can we see and act *clearly* in the current that is sweeping us along—those are the questions that I hope not so much to answer (who, indeed, could?) as simply to ask, and to give one example of the way in which we might try to solve them.

What follows, I realise, contains a profession of faith. But it is intended above all as the expression of an objective view of what is happening. I have written it without making the least claim to impose my views on others, but simply, as every scientific worker does, to make my own individual contribution to the common inquiry.

And it is in that spirit that I hope I shall be read.

1. *The essential belief: the future of man*

Underlying all the reactions aroused in us by the present events, we must recognise a robust faith in the future of mankind: and if that faith does already exist, we must consolidate it.

This duty is all the more urgent in that we can now see on all sides the ever latent sediment of pessimism and disillusion being stirred up by the wave we are riding on. With some, it is an only too natural emotional reaction to the disorders that upset their idea of a decently ordered bourgeois society. With others, it is an unspoken reaction against advances that might well prove that the future could be greater that the past. With others again, it represents a strange ideal of virtue—for them the 'strong' man is the man who can destroy the greatest number of illusions—in other words, hopes—that prevail in his circle. With some minds, it is perhaps also the desire to win an easy reputation for originality, by denying what others have painfully built up. How much, indeed, one has nowadays to listen to or read about the decay of civilisations or even the coming end of the world.

This defeatism (as an expression of temperament, as an attitude to the good, or simply as a pose) seems to me the fundamental temptation of the present day. It will readily be granted that it is unhealthy and ineffective; but it may be more difficult to prove that it is false. In other words, can we, as we look around us, find, not emotional or instinctive, but rational and objective reasons for believing that now, more than ever, we must have hope? I believe that we can; and it is this that I hope first to make clear.

A first reason for concluding that the present crisis is not a fatal disease seems to me to lie in the new form or structure assumed by mankind in the brief period of the last century. Only three or four generations ago, the world was still divided into isolated racial groups, whose potentials were so completely different that their mutual destruction seemed a possibility constantly to be feared. Today, the network of a common psychology stretches over the surviving differences of ancient cultures. In the space of a few years what we call modern civilisation has suddenly spread like a veil over the entire surface of the inhabited earth. In every country in the world men now know essentially the same things, and think on essentially the same lines. Surely this levelling up of human beings on a higher plane is a definitive guarantee of stability? I would be quite prepared to think so. Formerly mankind's treasures were confined in a library or an empire, and a fire or a military defeat was all that was needed to annihilate them. Now they are spread over the whole extent of the earth, and what cataclysm, short of the actual destruction of our planet, could threaten them? In short, by becoming generally extended to all peoples, civilisation seems to me to have passed through a critical point, from which it is emerging invulnerable to the attacks that caused the fall of Egypt, Rome, and Athens: it is like a huge liner that can safely cross seas in which an ancient galley would founder. What is no more than national may well disappear, but what is human cannot be lost.

This, however, is only half, and the negative half, of what we have to establish. What the pessimists or self-styled realists of today basically challenge is not so much the value, or even the stability, of the results that have been attained, as the possibility of a new advance. We must therefore take a further step if we are to dispose of them. There is no longer any danger of losing the ground we have won. Good—but does there lie ahead the possibility of rising still higher, of an even greater victory? Could we not find a factual reason that would assure us, in spite of any appearances to the contrary, not only that the past is a permanent acquisition but also that the future is ours?

I sincerely believe that such a reason for hope does indeed exist. And I think it is to be found in a way of looking at things which to my mind (even though its originators have not yet fully developed its implications) is the greatest discovery made by modern science: I mean the existence of a cosmic development of Spirit.

In the course of this last century, I was saying a moment ago, man came to feel that he encircled the whole earth. This new feeling is nothing beside the consciousness aroused in him at the same time of filling duration itself.

First of all, under the increasing influence of history, the past was revealed to us: not the few thousands of years that marked the horizon of Pascal or Bossuet or Newton—but the bottomless depths into which the series of physics, astronomy and biology henceforth plunge, as we follow them back till they are lost to view. For some time man could imagine that he floated, a new and independent creature, on the surface of this fathomless ocean. And then, by learning to focus his vision more correctly, he began to realise that those depths were in reality filled by himself. To anyone who can read today the pattern of facts recorded by science, mankind is no longer an accidental phenomenon that appeared by chance on one of the smallest stars in the heavens. It represents, in the field of our experience, the highest manifestation of the fundamental current that has gradually produced thought within matter. We are nothing more or less than that portion of the Weltstoff that has emerged into consciousness of self.

This view of the 'phenomenon of man' is completely different from the old anthropocentrism which made man the geometric and static centre of the universe: seeing man as a supremely characteristic form of the cosmic phenomenon, it has an incalculable moral range; it transforms the value and guarantees the immortality of the work we effect—or rather of the work that is effected through us. And here we have precisely the point that we must, I believe, take into consideration if we wish to reassure our minds in the face of the present crisis.

So long as mankind could be regarded as a fortunate anomaly, a brief epiphenomenon, in the vast processes of Nature, no consideration of the experimental order could reassure us about what I would go so far as to call the universe's dispositions in regard to us. One chance made us, and another chance might take us away. So long, moreover, as we had no more than six thousand years of recorded history with which to judge the shape of the human trajectory, it was permissible to argue endlessly whether civilisation is ascending or descending, or whether it is stagnating at a level that is always the same—or whether, again, it is following some hopeless sinusoid curve like that so skilfully drawn by Spengler.

All these anxieties and uncertainties disappear if we rise up high enough to see the true nature and the true dimensions of the fact of man. On the one hand there can be no doubt of the direction of the 'consciousness-phenomenon', of which our civilisation is provisionally, at the present moment, simply the ultimate expression; considered at a depth of the past that goes beyond the limits of history and human prehistory to include the whole history of the world, it shows positive variation; it grows—with local hesitations and mistakes, it is true—sometimes here, sometimes there—like a river seeking its bed —but without stopping, and still more without any general reversal. On the other hand, if this rise is indeed, as it seems, the effect of a 'cosmic tide', what local accident or what local dam could hold up the flow? It is here that the infantile aspect is shown up of the insinuations and objections by which the prophets of human failure seek to upset us. We are reminded of past catastrophes, or the physical and moral symptoms of decadence are detailed for us. All that, we must retort, is intellectual myopia. If we look at these terrifying events in the context of the total phenomenon, their irregularities are lost in the inexorable majesty and certainty of the over-all movement. Life has hitherto found its way round or has overthrown all the obstacles it has been meeting for millions of years. And would you have it that just because we are in the year 1936 this irresistible current, whose bed is the whole universe, is slowing down and beginning to flow backwards? It would be impossible. The transformation is so slow that if we observe the facts over a short period we may well fail to be conscious of it. But the whole of modern physics is at hand to witness that the most powerful trends recognised in the world today were first taken for models of immobility. The highly critical events taking place in the West today can be the effect only of progress. In spite of all apparent evidence to the contrary, we can and must believe this: *we are advancing.*

With this first result secured, we have still, if we are to build our faith in man on a solid foundation, to carry our inquiry further and ask ourselves the question that immediately arises: if we are advancing, in what direction are we moving?

This question would obviously be meaningless if what we were trying to do was to define in advance the particular human state towards which we are aiming. The forms to be assumed by the future are by their nature unpredictable. But the question takes on a very definite meaning, and has a possible solution, if we confine ourselves to asking in what direction, along what axes, is the metamorphosis of man effected. In other words, what conditions must the future satisfy if it is to be coherent with the present and the past?

I can see three.

The first is that an open horizon lie ahead of us, one that we may regard as *unlimited*. This is not the place to explore fundamentally the structural conditions of human action, nor critically to bring out this fact (never sufficiently emphasised) that our will cannot be set in motion except towards an object that has for it the savour of indestructibility. All I need say, to be understood by those who have the sense of life and the zest for it, is that no form of progress would appeal to us if we were unable to launch ourselves towards it with the consciousness that nothing could ever halt the forward movement. The reality towards which man rises must, by something in itself, be incorruptible and inexhaustible. If it is not to lose heart and automatically bring about its own destruction, the cosmic phenomenon of spiritualisation must be *irreversible*. That is a first attribute we must accord to the world that lies ahead of us.

While so vast as to offer no barrier to any possible development, the future must next, if it is to satisfy us, be seen to be so comprehensive that it excludes none of the positive elements now included in the universe. After irreversibility and incorruptibility, there must be *totality*; that is the second characteristic without which the future could not contain man's hopes. Here again, to be understood, I need only appeal to the evidence that every man can find if he looks deeply into himself. The only attractive form that (by an instinct that is readily reduced to exact reasons) we can give to the continuations of the world is that of a concentration from which nothing that is good or beautiful is left out: whether individuals, thoughts, or forces. This demand for the universal makes itself felt in the most intimate depths of the soul of each one of us; but we can recognise and confirm it in the general advance of human consciousness and even in the seemingly blindest development of the collective and material organisations we live among. However far back we may go in the history of philosophy and religions, the idea of a whole in process of formation has always been the pole with a magnetic attraction for the loftiest minds and the finest souls. And however clearly we may see into the determinisms that control us, the establishment, over the multiplicity of man, of an unbreakable social and economic network, pervading everything like the ether, is one of the most extraordinary phenomena ever offered to the speculation of physicists and biologists. Minds and matter once again unite to drive us irresistibly towards some higher unification.

An essential property must be distinguished and retained in this indefinite convergence in which the future of mankind is expressed for us, if our minds are to be fully satisfied by the notion of the future. The irreversible process that brings us together in some vast organic unity must not detract from but heighten *our personality*. That is the third and last condition that must be satisfied by the movement that carries us along, if we are to entrust ourselves to it. Of the reality of this requirement there seems to me to be no doubt—whether we base it on our instinct to survive—or whether, more critically, we analyse the cosmic significance and value of 'the personal'. We often speak of person as though it represented a form of total reality that is quantitatively reduced and qualitatively weakened. We should understand it in a directly opposite sense. The personal is the highest state in which we are able to apprehend the stuff of the universe. Moreover, something unique and incommunicable is concentrated, grain by grain, in its mysterious atomicity. The only way, accordingly, of expressing in a formula the fact that the world advances without ever retreating, or ever losing any part of itself, is to say that the quality and quantity of the personal it contains must constantly be increasing: *The universe* could not *logically* grow towards a spiritual totality if it did not rise up *to a state in which both it and each one of its elements were more fully self-centred.*[2] *As a fact*, that is indeed possible. At first, I know, an increasing personalisation of the universe seems to contradict the idea we have already accepted of its totalisation. Do not both theory and, unhappily, the facts of society seem to prove that individuals are stifled and destroyed by the progress of the collective? Here again I shall insist that this is certainly not true. If you look at the structure of living beings, in which the complexity of the cells goes hand in hand with the concentration of the whole organism; if you examine the psychology of comrades who are associated, freely to serve some great cause; if you consider the mutual fulfilment of two beings who love one another; if you analyse philosophically the effect of a centre on the elements it gathers together, and note that it

[2] Père Teilhard uses the English 'self' (*self-centrée*) (Tr.).

does not dissolve but inevitably completes them—in every case you will come to a conclusion that directly contradicts what first seemed to be indicated. True union does not run together the beings it joins, but rather differentiates them more fully: in other words, in the case of reflective particles, it ultra-personalises them. The whole is not the antipodes but the very pole of the person. Totalisation and personalisation are two manifestations of a single movement.[3]

Thus we have reached the end of our inquiry. *Futurism* (by which must be understood the existence of a boundless sphere of improvements and discoveries), *Universalism*, and *Personalism*: those are the three characteristics of the progress that leads us on, with the whole mass and the whole infallibility of the universe behind it. And these, in consequence, are the three unshakeable axes upon which our faith in man's effort can and must rest with complete assurance. Futurism, Universalism, Personalism: the three pillars on which the future rests.

2. *The process to be distinguished: the convergence of man*

Basing ourselves firmly on the point of view we have just established, we can now safely turn back and look again at the troubles that are harassing the world at the present moment. We have now mastered the factors that are necessary first to appreciate the true nature of our situation and then to decide what measures we should take while the storm still rages. This is what we now have to be clear about in our minds.

Most important of all, what exactly is going on today deep down in the human mass? We know, indeed, that we are advancing, but why is there such disorder all round us?

We started this inquiry by saying that at this moment three

---

[3] This is obviously only the outline of a theory that would call for much lengthier elaboration to be absolutely clear.

main influences, apart from Christianity, are confronting one another, each fighting for the possession of the earth: democracy, communism, and fascism. Where does the strength of these three currents come from? And why is the battle between them so implacable?

We may, I think, start to find the way to the solution of this new problem in a preliminary observation that everybody could have made, but whose significance became apparent only in the course of our first section: in each of the three masses confronting one another, there can distinctly be recognised, though still rudimentary and incomplete, the very three aspirations which we saw to be the characteristics of faith in the future. Passion for what is still to come, passion for the universal, passion for the personal—all three wrongly or imperfectly understood—that is the threefold driving force which, in our world today, sets in tension and opposes to one another the energies of man. Before we deduce the consequences of this, let us just verify the fact.

In the case of democracy it is obvious enough. Democracy, as the first-born daughter of 'revolutionary' progress has grown up with the enthusiastic hope of limitless earthly improvements. Closer than any other to the fiery source from which emerged the consciousness of modern man, it still remains permeated by that original incandescence; but for the same reason, too, it contains the inflexibility and naiveté that often characterise the first manifestations of the truth. Two errors in perspective, logically linked, combine to weaken and corrupt the democratic view of the world: one affects its personalism, and the other, in consequence, its universalism.

Apart from Christianity, no spiritual movement has ever understood and exalted the value of the human person so much as the French Revolution. The apostles of 1789, unfortunately, were so carried away by their zeal for liberty that they did not realise that the social element takes on its full

138

individuality and its full value only in a whole within which it is differentiated. Instead of attaining freedom itself, it has brought a general emancipation. Thereby each cell has believed itself to be justified in setting itself up as a centre for its own self. From this arose the fragmentation, condemned by the facts, of the false intellectual and social forms of liberalism; and from this, again, the ruinous and impossible egalitarianism that threatens every serious attempt to build up a new earth. By showing the people the direction followed by progress, democracy seems to satisfy the idea of totality; in fact what it offers is a counterfeit. True universalism claims, it is true, to invite all forms of initiative without exception, all value, all the most hidden potentialities, to share in its syntheses; but it is essentially organic and hierarchic. By confusing individualism and personalism, mob and totality—by fragmentation and levelling-down of the human mass—democracy was well on the way to jeopardising the hopes, born with it, of a future for man. That is why it has seen communism detach itself to the left, and, on the right, all the forms of fascism range themselves in opposition.

In communism, faith in a universal human organisation is, or at any rate was originally, magnificently exalted. This can never be insisted on too emphatically. What constitutes the temptation, for an élite, of Russian neo-Marxism is not so much its humanitarian gospel as its vision of a totalitarian civilisation, firmly linked to the cosmic powers of matter. Communism could more truly be called 'Terrenism'. There is a real appeal in this enthusiasm for the earth's resources and its future. Moreover, for the last twenty years, all the facts have been demonstrating the spiritual power hidden in the gospel of Lenin. No modern movement has ever succeeded (at least spasmodically) in creating such an atmosphere of newness and universality. Unhappily, in that quarter, too, the human ideal is seriously incomplete or distorted. In the first place, through

too sharp a reaction against the anarchistic liberalism of democracy, communism has come practically to destroy the person
and to make man into a termite. Secondly, in its unbalanced
admiration for the tangible forces of the world, it has systematically turned its hopes away from the possibilities of a spiritual metamorphosis of the universe. The Phenomenon of Man
(which, as we have seen, is essentially defined by the development of thought) is thus reduced to the mechanical development of a soulless collectivity. Matter has cast a veil over
Spirit. A pseudo-determinism has killed love. The absence of
personalism, entailing a limitation or even a perversion of the
future, and thereby cutting the ground from under the possibility and even the very notion of universalism—these, much
more than any economic upheavals constitute the dangers of
Bolshevism.

If we now turn to fascism, we shall see that it can hardly be
doubted that the fascist movement was born largely as a
reaction to ideas that are commonly associated with the Revolution. This origin explains the compromising support it has
constantly found among numerous elements in whose interest
it is (for various reasons of intellectual and social conservatism)
not to believe in a future for man. The static, however, can
never command our passionate adherence; and certainly
there is no lack of ardour in fascism. Where, then, does it find
its fire? Clearly enough, in that same threefold faith that animates the currents to which it is the most bitterly opposed.
Fascism opens its arms to the future. Its ambition is to embrace vast wholes in its empire. And in the vigorous organisation of which it dreams, it is more anxious than any other
system to allow for the preservation of the élite (which means
the personal and the Spirit) and to make good use of it. *Within
the field it seeks to cover*, then, its constructions satisfy more fully
perhaps than any others the conditions we have recognised as
essential to the city of the future. The only, but the massive,

misfortune is that the field it has in mind is so ridiculously limited. So far, fascism seems to wish to ignore the critical human transformation and the irresistible material bonds that have now permanently introduced civilisation to the stage of internationalism. It persists in thinking of the modern world which lives in it, and in bringing it into effective being, as though its dimensions were still 'neolithic'. The result of this lack of proportion is that it offers us only a restricted picture of the future of which we dream; what it lacks is precisely the essential quality which distinguishes the total from the partial, the finite from the limitless. Fascism may possibly represent a fairly successful small-scale model of tomorrow's world. It may perhaps be a necessary stage in the course of which men have to learn, as though on a smaller training-ground, their human role. But it will become what we are waiting for only if, when the time comes, it abandons the narrow nationalism that obliges it to exclude from its constructions all the elements that really come up to the scale of the earth—the nationalism that causes it to press on into the future in the hope of finding again forces of civilisation that are lost for ever.

Now that our analysis is finished, we may stop and consider. The three characteristics (futurism, personalism, universalism) which define the direction of the human drive have given us the key; and with it we can read the secrets of the great modern motive forces in society: the mainsprings that drive them are exposed to view. I come back, then, to the question I asked before: what is happening at this moment to the human mass? Why is there this violence, and why these clashes? And I think I am beginning to understand.

Confronted by today's quarrels, we might well fear (as the chorus of pessimists threatens us) that we were witnessing the retrogression and dissolution of civilisation. We may now, however, be completely reassured: both *a priori* (in virtue of

141

the general principle that the Phenomenon of Man contains in itself something that is infallible), and *a posteriori* (from our observation of the events that are unfolding). In the first place, the forces that confront one another all around us are not forces of destruction: each of them includes positive components. Secondly, by sharing those same components, they are not moving further away from one another, but are converging, in a hidden way, towards a common concept of the future. Thirdly, and this explains their implacable nature, in each one of them it is the world itself that is on the defensive and is struggling towards the light.

Fragments that are seeking one another, and not fragments that are parting from one another, a world that is striving for unity, not a world that is disintegrating. A crisis of birth, and not symptoms of death. Essential affinities and not undying hate.

That is what we are witnessing: and we have only to discern that beneath the currents and in the storm to realise what action we must take to be saved.

3. *What must be done: the human front*

If there is any solid basis to the above considerations, if, that is, the present troubles do indeed express an effort on the part of modern mankind to find its soul, then our duty is clear. It is to help, with all our strength, the birth of the new world that is trying to emerge.

We have seen what are the chief characteristics of this new earth. Faith in a limitless future, in which all the positive values of civilisation will be united in a totality that emphasises individual values. A higher passion in which three things will be both re-included and consummated in a new synthesis: the democratic sense of the rights of the person, the communist vision of the powers of matter, and the fascist ideal of organised élites. That is the '*fourth spirit*' which is coming to maturity, and for which we are all waiting. We must develop our own consciousness of this, and proclaim it far and wide.

Fundamentally, and in spite of the (relative) enthusiasm that draws large sections of mankind into the political and social currents of the day, the mass of mankind is still unsatisfied. For my own part, I do not know either on the right or on the left any truly progressive thinker who does not admit that he is to some degree disappointed by all the existing movements. Men join one party or another, simply because, in order to act, a choice must be made. But every man feels that in the place he fills he is ill at ease, incomplete as a man, and disgusted. We are looking for something wider, more comprehensive, and finer.

This far-reaching disquiet would, I am sure, immediately settle down if only it could succeed in formulating the programme, the ideal, of which we all dream. Our fathers of old set out on the great adventure in the name of justice and the rights of man. They did not understand, nor could they know, that the harmony whose anticipation they found so intoxicating required for its realisation a dimension for the future the very idea of which had not yet been conceived. They still saw the world too much with the simple eyes of the shepherd, as an idyll—not as a discovery and a conquest. We who now have the whole of Space and the whole of Time in which to develop the only liberty, the only equality, the only fraternity that are possible (those that is, that are born from collaboration in a common task)—we must rise up in turn, as one man, as champions of the rights of the world, in the names (not so abstract, either, as might be thought) of the future, the universal, and the person.

We have all had quite enough (not to put it more strongly) of the nationalist sectarianisms that wall off human sympathies, and of the claims of a mob that remains profoundly antagonistic and impotent, so long as it does not cease, by becoming personalised, to be a mob. We are locked up in a prison where we cannot breathe. We must have air. We do not want fascist fronts, or a popular front—but a *human front*.

And, as I said before, we can find all around us the elements with which to build this front, at once solidly united and progressive, scattered throughout the apparently hostile masses who are fighting one another. All they need to orientate themselves and join together is a shock. If once the requisite ray of light falls upon those fragmented hordes, if once they can hear the call that appeals to their inmost structure, then, cutting across all the party loyalties and conventional barriers that still exist, we shall see the living atoms of the earth seeking one another out, finding one another and becoming organised.

Look deeply enough and you will find that there are only two classes of men in the human race: those who stake their soul on a future greater than themselves, and those who through inertia, selfishness, or because they have lost heart, have no wish to press on. Those who believe in what is to come and those who do not. Every political party today is unconsciously poisoned by a mixture of these contradictory essences. The formation of a human front would put an end to all such ambivalence. The regrouping of forces, effected on the basis of a fundamental concept of being, would bring out into the open the living energies of civilisation. And thus, for perhaps the first time, the '*good*' and the '*bad' could recognise one another and take each other's measure*. There would then perhaps be war between the two camps representing the two attitudes of belief or non-belief in the spiritual future of the universe, the only essential war that lay disguised under all the other wars: the final, open, war between inertia and progress; the conflict between what climbs up and what sinks back. The splendour, at least, ad the issue of such a battle would never be in doubt; and those who took part in it would

144

(at last) not have to fear, at any rate, that they were firing on their own kin.

It will be objected to the formation of this human party, or rather super-party, that its coming into being would call, even more than for a well-defined general aspiration, for the existence of a common antagonist. When it comes to constructive work, it will be said, agreement is never possible. Only fear has hitherto been found capable of producing unanimity. From this it follows that the terrestrial universality of a human effort cannot be expected from a hope. In order to create it a universal terrestrial enemy must appear. For my own part, I do not believe in the supreme effectiveness of the instinct of preservation and of fear. It was not the terror of being lost but the ambition to live that drove man to the exploration of nature, to the conquest of the ether, and to finding his way in the air. At the same time I recognise that an abstract formula is not sufficient to set us in motion and make us cohere. The lodestone that will have to magnetise in us the energies whose increasing overspill is at present being dissipated in useless clashes or in perverse refinements will ultimately, I believe, be found in the possible revelation of some essential object: this, in all the richness it holds, will be more precious than any gold and have more attractive power than any beauty, and would be for man, now adult, the Grail and Eldorado dreamed of by the conquerors of old: something tangible, to possess which it would be infinitely good to give one's life.

That is why, if a human front began to be formed, there would have to be, besides the engineers who were concerned with organising the resources of the earth and its structural links, other 'technicians' whose sole business it would be to define and extend the knowledge of the more and more exalted concrete goals on which the effort of human activities must be concentrated. Hitherto we have, and with reason, developed a passionate interest in the revelation of the mysteries

145

that lie hidden in what is infinitely large and infinitely small in matter; but a much more important investigation for the future would be the study of the currents and magnetic forces whose *nature is psychic*: in fact, an energetics of spirit. Driven by the necessity to build up the unity of the world, we may, perhaps, come in the end to see that the great work dimly guessed at and pursued by science is simply the discovery of God.

4. The place of Christianity

Even if I were not a Christian, writing here for Christians, I should have to include Christianity in this analysis of human currents: not only because Christianity, either directly or by its influence, still controls a large part of modern civilisation, but even more because its life is deeply involved in the present conflict.

I started by saying that Christians feel themselves to be exceptionally sensitive to the struggle which at this moment is bringing into conflict the forces of fascism, communism, and democracy. To some small extent only this arises from the fact that the new institutions are sooner or later forced to take up positions in the moral and social sphere which conflict with the gospel. From our earlier observations we can now understand more clearly that under the political top-dressing of the battles now being fought, today's struggle is in reality between opposing general views of life and the world. The rudiments of a 'human faith' are coming to light, and they are tending to become organised in a new religion. It is in consequence the very foundations of the human *anima religiosa*, on which the Church had been building for two thousand years, that are changing in dimensions and nature. It is hardly surprising, then, that the whole building is rocked by this deep-seated movement.

146

If we ask how Christianity should react to the transformation that is taking place, not only in such a way that it may survive but so that, in saving us, it may grow greater, I would, in conclusion, make the following suggestion.

The problem of the present relations between Christianity and Humanism remains obscure so long as we do not succeed in reducing the two antagonistic forces to their common factors. On the other hand, it seems to me to be solved without difficulty as soon as we see that the guiding principles of Christ's religion are exactly the same as those in which we found the essence of human effort expressed: Heaven, Catholicity, the City of souls; in other words, futurism, universalism, personalism. If the axes of faith are so alike for the follower of Christ and the followers of the earth, a comparison of them, term to term, should be possible, and even a conflation. This is the method I have tried to follow; and the result I have arrived at is as follows. On two out of the three points under consideration (the only two on which agreement would seem difficult to obtain—I mean futurism and personalism), Christianity is not only not opposed to Humanism but provides it with exactly the complement without which terrestrial faith cannot reach its full and complete development. Thus agreement between the two forces is possible. Let us look at this more closely.

First, futurism. We have already accepted as a fact, though without trying to find the conditions that make it physically possible, the 'unlimited' character which man, if he is to act, must necessarily be able to attribute to his future. Now as soon as we try to realise this quality objectively within the framework of the universe of experience, we find that it tends to break through the present limits of Nature. What, in fact, in relation to our boundless demands, are the few hundreds of millions of years that the most generous astronomers give the earth? And what, moreover, would be the state,

147

after a term of imprisonment of such a duration, of a mankind that is already beginning to feel cramped on our small planet? If we think about it, there can be no true future except on the hypothesis (and hope) of some critical threshold that would allow the world, precisely under the influence of its physical development, to pass into a state different from that in which we know it. Now that, surely, is exactly the truth maintained by the Christian faith. Not only do 'the new heaven and the new earth' anticipated by the gospel, open up (if we are prepared to 'homogenise' them with our modern representations of the world), unexpected horizons to the physics of matter—but they provide the only space in which one of the most essential qualities of our psychological being can be deployed—irreversibility in progress and ambitions.

Next, personalism. The gravest danger that lies in wait for humanity on its present course is finally to forget the essential thing, that is, spiritual concentration, when confronted with the cosmic immensities disclosed to it by science, and with the collective power revealed to it by social organisation. A diffuse energy, or a heartless, faceless, super-society, are not these the forms in which the terrestrial neo-religion tries in a confused way to represent the Deity? In this perilous phase which threatens the existence of 'souls', it is Christianity, I feel, that can and will intervene to bring human aspirations back to the only line that conforms to the structural laws of being and of life. Even yesterday it could be thought that nothing was so out of date, so anthropomorphic, as the personal God of Christianity. And now, in this aspect of its creed, seemingly so antiquated and yet the most essential, the Christian gospel is seen to be the most modern of religions. Christianity is now confronted by a mankind which is in danger of allowing that part of consciousness which has already been aroused in it by the progress of life, to be swallowed up in the 'secondary matter' of philosophical determinisms and social mechanisms. Against this, Christianity maintains the primacy of reflective, that is to say personalised, thought: and this it does in the most effective of all ways. It does not confine itself to defending theoretically by its teaching the possibility of a centred but at the same time universal consciousness; it goes much further, and through its mysticism it transmits and develops the sense and in some way the direct intuition of this Centre of total convergence. The least the modern non-believer must admit, if he understands the biological situation of the world, is that the figure of Christ (not simply the dream figure of literature but its concrete realisation in the Christian consciousness) is the closest and most perfect approach yet effected to a final and total object to which the universal effort of man can be directed without ever wearying or losing its true character.

Thus, contrary to a frequently accepted idea, it is not so much in its moral teaching as in its dogma that Christianity is human, and it is on that ground that tomorrow it may well be called upon once again to save the world. What, then, is the reason for the sort of disrepute this very dogma seems to have earned for Christianity in the eyes of those who work so hard for a greater mankind? Why the suspicion, why the hatred?

The developments arising from the conflict between faith and progress have done more harm to Christianity than the most savage persecutions; and the reason for the conflict will be found, I believe, in a lack of adjustment which affects the three components of the Christian spirit, the futurist, the universalist, and the personalist. Christianity is universalist; but it has remained too long attached to a medieval cosmology, instead of resolutely facing the temporal and spatial immensities to which the facts insist it must extend its views of the Incarnation. Christianity is supremely futurist; but the very transcendence of the views it maintains has led it to allow itself to be regarded as *extra-terrestrial* (and so passive and soporific), whereas by the sheer logic of its dogma it should be

149

supra-terrestrial (and should therefore be the generator of a maximum human effort). Finally, Christianity is specifically personalist; but here again the predominance allowed to the values of the soul has inclined it to offer itself as primarily a juridical and moral system, instead of showing us the organic and cosmic splendours enclosed in its universal Christ.

I believe that Christianity can and must impose itself upon the new human soul that is being born in a world torn by such convulsions, to set its mark upon it and raise it up; but, to bring about that salvation there is one condition it must satisfy—it must, following out the implications of its own creed, be reincarnated, which means that it must frankly and resolutely fall into line with what we have called the human front.

This alignment will not prevent it from being attacked by those who reproach it for leading us too far afield or too high; but at least there will be an end to that fatal misunderstanding which so often results in our being attacked by those who are fundamentally our friends and allies.

A Christian can joyfully suffer persecution in order that the world may grow greater. He can no longer accept death on the charge that he is blocking mankind's road.

Peking, 11 November 1936[4]

---

[4] An abridged version was published under the title 'La Crise Présente' in *Études*, 20 October 1937, and in Cahier 3 of the Association des amis de P. Teilhard de Chardin: *Teilhard de Chardin et la Politique africaine*, Paris, 1962.

CHAPTER X

SUPER-HUMANITY, SUPER-CHRIST, SUPER-CHARITY[1]

SOME NEW DIMENSIONS FOR THE FUTURE

From many indications (all sorts of dissatisfactions and aspirations) it is clear that a profound and general transformation is taking place at present in the consciousness of man. Intellectually, morally and mystically, we are no longer satisfied with what was good enough for our fathers. We *are looking for* something better. But while the fact of this internal change is undeniable, to define its nature and its causes is quite another problem. Year after year, I have been trying in a series of essays to isolate and pin down the hidden source of our anxious questioning and the elusive substance of our expectations.

What follows here contains nothing that I have not already said on the same subject elsewhere, but it is presented from a different angle.

I recently suggested (in *The New Spirit*[2]) that what makes us so different from earlier generations, and so much more demanding, is the awakening of our consciousness to a new setting that is cosmic in dimensions: *the cone of Time*. In this particular environment, which diverges endlessly to the rear but converges positively ahead, an unexpected link can be seen, I said, between determinisms and liberty, between totalisation and personalisation and between immanent evolution and

---

[1] The prefix 'super' is used in these three words to indicate not a difference of *nature* but a more advanced *degree* of realisation or perception. (Author's note.)

[2] In *The Future of Man*, Collins, London, and Harper & Row, New York, 1964, p. 82. (Ed.)

creation, which assists the development of spirit. It is precisely this that is needed to harmonise in us the seemingly antagonistic impulses that now divide our innate powers of worship between man, the universe, and Christ.

I believe that today this same solution can profitably be expressed in a less synthetic way but with more practical urgency, if we start not from a change in the curve followed by our experience but from a change of scale in its totality. What is it, when all is said and done, that in these days makes all the fibres of our hearts and minds vibrate so painfully and with such passion, but the sudden transition from the intermediate to the immense? To put it more exactly, what is it that, in a way difficult to define, is upsetting the whole system of our traditional habits, but the irresistible emergence deep within us of three 'super-realities', closely linked with one another?

A Super-humanity, on the scale of the earth.

A Super-Christ, on the scale of that Super-humanity.

A Super-charity, on the scale both of the Super-Christ and of Super-humanity.

So far as I am concerned, I find it impossible not to see this in myself and in those I move among. And this is what, without any ulterior motive of belittling any traditional position, I shall try to make plain to others—not as a speculative fancy but as an undeniable psychological fact.

I. SUPER-HUMANITY

By Super-humanity I mean the higher biological state that mankind seems destined to attain if, carrying to its extreme limit the process from which it historically emerged, it succeeds in becoming completely totalised upon itself, body and soul.

So defined, Super-humanity is not, as we are often told to

believe, a speculative or emotional entity, a dream or an utopia; but, although most people do not yet suspect it, it already represents a reality, or at least the imminence of a reality *of the scientific order*; and it would therefore be as useless to try to rebel against it as it would be to try to halt the march of the solar system or the cooling of the earth.

In this first chapter, then, we shall consider briefly:

1. How, on the authority of our most certain knowledge, the eventual appearance of a Super-humanity seems biologically inevitable.

2. With what general characteristics this Super-humanity is taking shape.

3. And finally what new spiritual attitude is being imposed upon us by the prospect we thus anticipate.

A. REALITY

If we arrange them in their logical order, the cumulative and convergent indications which, taken as a whole, *oblige* us, I am convinced, to regard as certain the coming appearance of a Super-humanity, may be expressed as follows.

First of all, *the historical reality*, well attested in the past, of a *gradual ascent of mankind*. This evolution covers, at the lowest estimate, a hundred or two hundred thousand years, and we are still a long way from knowing all its details. What we do know, however, is enough to determine unmistakably the curve followed by the phenomenon. From the distant prehominians (Pithecanthropus, Sinanthropus) to *Homo sapiens*, running through the complex Neanderthaloid group, a movement can definitely be recorded, which drives the human group from states that are *slightly*, to states that are *highly*, cerebralised and socialised.[3] On one side (that of the

---

[3] In two orders that differ in magnitude, cerebralisation and socialisation are basically the same thing: since in the case of man socialisation causes the individuals simply to associate and organise their reflective activities, that is to say

prehominians) we have an extremely low level of brain and loose or scattered ethnic groups; on the other (that of modern man) an extremely high level of brain, and, particularly since the Neolithic age, a continually more rapid advance towards the collective.

It is impossible, in my view, for anyone who thinks about it honestly, to look at the results already obtained by prehistory without recognising that he is forced to accept the objective reality of an anthropogenesis in the past—and in consequence (this is the decisive point) without realising that he is equally forcibly obliged to admit some continuation of this same anthropogenesis in the future.

So far, and for as long as we know it, mankind has constantly been moving towards ascending states of psychic organisation. If that is admitted, there is no reason—indeed it would be illogical—to think that it should not still be moving in the same direction. Behind us, there undoubtedly lies a 'sub-humanity'. Ahead of us, therefore, and just as certainly, there must be a Super-humanity: the only reality, we may note incidentally, that is capable of occupying and justifying the *millions* of years that still perhaps remain for the development of thought on earth.

In that form, let me remind you, this demonstration, based solely on human palaeontology, of the world's drift to psychic states higher than at present, is as convincing as the majority of proofs on which the most widely accepted of our scientific beliefs are based. It has, however, the disadvantage of applying to a relatively restricted body of facts over a short period of time. It may well be objected that a hundred million years is still not very long for determining with certainty the trajec-

their brains. This fundamental biological identity between individual cerebralisation and socialisation (or *collective cerebralisation*), so clearly noted by Julian Huxley and many others, is a basic *scientific* concept, which the reader must fully grasp if he is to understand anything that follows in this essay.

154

tory of anthropogenesis. Who can say whether, if it were observed over a longer period, the curve might not take some other shape, descending, perhaps, or sinusoid? Moreover, does not man, in his mental properties, represent an exceptional case, a unique and therefore unpredictable pattern of behaviour in Nature?

Two complementary series of observations, allow us, I believe, to remove this latter doubt: one establishes what I shall call *the biological law of cephalisation*, and the other *the cosmic law of complexity*.

First, the law of cephalisation. Whatever the animal group (vertebrate or arthropod) whose evolution we study, it is a remarkable fact that in every case the nervous system increases with time in volume and organisation, and at the same time concentrates in the frontal, cephalic, region of the body. Considered in the detail of limbs and of skeleton, the various organic types can, it is true, become differentiated, each along its own line, in the most diverse or opposite directions; but considered in the development of the cerebral ganglia, all life, the whole of life, drifts (sometimes more rapidly, sometimes less, but always with an essential drift), like a single rising flood, in the direction of the largest brains.

Secondly, the law of complexity. For a long time physical chemistry concentrated on the phenomena of atomic disintegration, whose effect is to reduce matter to continually more advanced states of pluralisation and simplicity; now, however, it is turning its attention to the converse movement, which, in the temperate zones of the universe such as our earth, is tending to group molecules in super-molecules that are more and more formidably complicated. Continuing this line of natural syntheses, an unexpected prospect is revealed, in which the sciences of matter and of life meet together. At extreme degrees of physico-chemical complexity, attaining the order of a million atoms, particles become 'animate'. At the level of the viruses we meet an ill-defined frontier which separates living from non-living beings. And if we now admit that beyond that frontier the significant part of cosmic complexification is concentrated on the building up of nervous systems, two further points must be accepted: that the movement is being carried even further and, what is more, that it coincides exactly, in its continuation, with the process, already independently recognised, of cephalisation.

Once that is established, everything in the evolution that carries us along becomes clear, as I promised, and takes on consistence. Since anthropogenesis incontestably represents (through its two terms, cerebralisation and socialisation) an extreme example of the law of cephalisation; and since the law of cephalisation is itself only the higher form assumed among living beings by the law of complexity, there can no longer be any ambiguity in our interpretation of the Phenomenon of Man. While the allied rise of brain and consciousness was observed only in the narrow field of human history, there could, I admitted, be some doubt about the stability of the process, or even about its real existence. Now, however, that this advance fits in, as a natural sequel and climax, with a movement that covers the whole biological and atomic history of the earth, the certainty of our first intuition is finally justified and firmly established.

We can, and indeed must, now face the coming, ahead of us, of a Super-humanity—not on the fallacious grounds of a seemingly favourable local accident, but supported and upheld by the general impulse of a universe in course of emergence.

B. WHAT FORM WILL SUPER-HUMANITY ASSUME?

While we may be convinced of the existence of something (God, the immortal soul, or, to take more simple examples, the other side of the moon, or the interior of the earth), it constantly happens that, for all our conviction, we are unable to say what the thing looks like. However solidly established, then, the existence of future super-human states may be, we may well be unable to determine their appearance. In this particular case, in fact, the position is not so desperate intellectually as might at first be feared. Without, indeed, allowing ourselves to be drawn in that quarter into the construction of concrete images (amusing, and even instructive, it is true, but ultimately false and absurd) we can perfectly well succeed in determining, with a good chance of probability, the conditions that Super-humanity must satisfy *if it is to exist*: first the fact of its existence, and then, in the most general terms, its form. To do this, we have only to continue (to extrapolate) with the necessary caution, the curve of anthropogenesis we established earlier. For some two hundred thousand years or more, we agreed, mankind as a whole has not ceased to advance in the direction of higher cerebralisation and closer socialisation. If, as everything warrants our anticipating, the movement continues further, in what form is it doing so, and towards what forms of man are we moving?

So far as individual cerebralisation is concerned, nothing justifies our asserting, but many signs give reason for supposing, that since its arrival at the *sapiens* level the human brain has to all intents and purposes reached the absolute limit imposed by the corpuscular laws of matter on the complexity of an *isolated* organic unit. In the course of the last twenty thousand years, in fact, no appreciable change has been produced in this quarter; and there is only a slight decrease of facial 'prognathism' (shown in a progressive disappearance of the 'wisdom teeth') to give us grounds for supposing that the human skull is still continuing in us to become more compact and rounded. If we wish to remain on solid ground, even though it may mean that we are falling short of reality, we must admit that along this first line of individual cerebralisation anthropogenesis has reached the end of its course; let us consider, then, the areas still open to collective cerebralisation or socialisation.

In this second quarter, an immense, a boundless, horizon is revealed. Let us make an effort to grasp in our minds, first town by town, then country by country, and continent by continent, the formidable multitude of 'thinking elements' scattered at this moment over the face of the earth. Let us try mentally to realise what this constantly increasing population of two thousand million human beings represents in *still diffuse* spiritual richness and spontaneity. This enormous plurality does not normally make much impression upon us; or rather we try to close our eyes to it, because it would terrify us and stifle us like some blind proliferation let loose upon us. Now, however, with the knowledge we have gained from the past of man and of life, all we have to do is to effect the reversal of our views suggested by the natural laws of cephalisation and complexity. We must make up our minds to associate together the ideas of cerebralisation and socialisation. Immediately the whole appearance of the earth is changed thereby, and it becomes intelligible to us.

In the first place, the aimless busyness of man that hitherto we found so disconcerting, takes the form of a *potential*—a potential all the more vast in that the world's lack of organisation is even more extensive. If the countless reflective elements now spread out over the face of the globe do indeed represent in their diversity so much material held in preparation for some possible structure, what an edifice may we not expect from it in the future![4]

Secondly, any number of compulsions that hitherto we used passively to accept, are rationally justified and take on meaning. The forces of external compression, in the first place,

---

[4] Considered in his collective (or social) cerebralisation, notes Julian Huxley, man is still approximately at the batrachian stage.

which are packing together more and more closely on the closed surface of our planet, a rapidly increasing number of elements whose individual radius of action is continually increasing; and at the same time the forces of internal infiltration that break through the barriers of our inner private life and make us, even in spite of ourselves, every day more one in our common thoughts and enthusiasms; all these forces from within and without are ceasing to be a bondage. Under the multiple influences that are cementing and forging us is it not in fact anthropogenesis continuing its work of hominisation?

The more we look at the human mass in this light, in its double aspect of horrifying incompleteness and inexorable drawing together, the less possible it becomes to dismiss the evidence that we are *here and now* the subjects of a profound organic transformation that is *collective in type*. Whatever improvements in the human nervous system may still be expected, this particular modification, it would seem, already represents no more than a secondary and subordinate event within the total phenomenon. It is not in the direction of anatomically super-cerebralised individuals that we must look if we are scientifically to discern the form assumed by Super-humanity, but in that of super-socialised aggregations.

There is, however, an important reservation or precaution that must be emphasised before we go any further.

There is nothing new in the idea of comparing mankind, taken as one whole, to a 'brain of brains' or to an ant-colony; but, unless they are to lead us into gross misrepresentations, these attractive analogies can be pursued only if they respect the human particle's quite unique property of constituting a reflective nucleus centred upon itself.

Below man in the evolutionary ladder of complexities, animate units behave *chiefly* either as links or as gears, in the phyla and social wholes to which they belong. *They transmit, rather than exist.*

Starting with man, however, there is a change in conditions. As a specific result of the phenomenon of 'reflexion', the living particle definitively closes in on itself. It begins to act and react as a centre of *incommunicable* value, a value therefore that cannot be transmitted. It lives for itself, as much as and at the same time as for others. It is *personalised*.

This does not mean, as some scientifically and morally disastrous theories hold, that starting with and by reason of its emergence into thought the individual human being is released from every nexus and further development in the phyletic and collective plane—as though the universe culminated in it. It has, however, this important consequence: in virtue of his particular corpuscular nature, man has become structurally incapable of entering as a stable element into any 'complexity' of a higher order unless its effect would be to preserve or even heighten his state and degree of personality.

In the case of man, therefore, collectivisation, super-socialisation, can only mean *super-personalisation*; in other words it ultimately means (since only the forces of love have the property of personalising by uniting) sympathy and *unanimity*.

It is in the direction and in the form of a single 'heart' that we must look for our picture of super-mankind, rather even than in that of a single brain.

C. PRE-INFLUENCE

The coming of a Super-mankind is guaranteed by all that we know of the past progress of the universe; in our time this can be seen, by the informed observer, in a network of political, economic and psychological relationships that are daily making it a little more impossible for us to live, to think, to seek, *by ourselves*;—but this is by no means all: if I am not mistaken, its approach is making itself directly felt in a characteristic transformation of the most urgent and deep-rooted evidence provided by our own consciousness.

Under the influence of the increasing collectivisation of man, we are beginning to have a more critical appreciation of the conditions required for the natural play of our freedom and action—and in consequence we are distinguishing more clearly the conditions of reality which the universe that contains us must satisfy if we are to be able to live in it.

This is what I still have to show.

1. *The new requirements for action*

So long as the human individual is conscious of living and working only for himself, he is not prepared to be too particular about the value and the ultimate fate of what is produced by his activities. He has, it is true, a rather vague ambition *to fulfil himself*, and to leave behind him some evidence of his passage through life; but at the same time he is too conscious of the uncertainties and chances of life to flatter himself that he—a single element lost in the multitude—can be successful and survive.

On the other hand, as the increasing clarity of the facts begins to impress upon him that his own true end lies far ahead and above in the Term of a super-human organisation, so he becomes aware of a legitimate increase in the scope of his ambitions and of his demands. At the level of the individual, failure and death may well appear to be no more than statistically inevitable accidents. At the level of the whole, they are seen to be an inadmissible catastrophe. *The end of the whole is not of the same order as the ends of the elements.* Or, to put it more exactly, its nature is such that it cannot be an 'end' closed in on itself; it cannot be a dead stop.

This, I believe, explains the gradual and irresistible awakening of the sense of (or rather the demand for) infallibility and irreversibility built into human activity. Man is more and more explicitly refusing to serve life except on the condition that his efforts, his discoveries and his progress, shall represent an advance that cannot end in failure and cannot fall back. I am well aware of the objections, both logical and psychological, by which a certain agnostic or 'realist' philosophy seeks to undermine the solidity of this intuition; but I believe that these destructive analyses cannot stand up against the necessarily biological character of the phenomenon. Just as reasoning cannot stop the earth from revolving, life from climbing upwards, intelligence from seeking to understand, and mankind from fusing into one—so it cannot prevail against the reality of a drift that, as we can see for ourselves, is carrying with it and transforming the entire mass of the thinking earth. We can dismiss as irrelevant the idea that earlier generations may have developed in this connexion—those for whom the dimension of duration did not yet exist nor the notion of evolution. So far as the men of today are concerned, however, I maintain that now that their sensibilities have been awakened by the first rays of Super-mankind rising over the horizon, they would stifle in a closed and reversible anthropogenesis just as surely as they would if oxygen were to disappear from the earth's atmosphere. It is a demand that we cannot perhaps explain, since it is more primordial than any of the other factual elements in our consciousness—but it is a demand that we must nevertheless admit as an essential characteristic of the evolutionary current that holds us up and carries us along.

2. A new universe

When, a moment ago, we were concluding our inquiry into the form to be assumed by the future of man, we said that on any hypothesis Super-mankind cannot be conceived except as super-personal. This is inevitably entailed by the reflective nature of human particles, which, it is clear, cannot develop less 'centricity' in the course of a transformation whose effect is to super-centre the universe upon itself.

If we now take a further step, we shall find that super-mankind cannot continue to develop unless the elements that freely associate in it can see in themselves evidence that the operation they are involved in is irreversible. This is entailed by the *total* nature of the end to be attained and to be accepted as paramount.

Let us, in conclusion, combine these two enabling conditions imposed by the stuff of the cosmos on the developments of anthropogenesis. Let us, in other words, ask what ultimate goal will be arrived at by a system of personal, and therefore incommunicable, elements that is subjected to a movement of personalisation (that is, of centration), if that movement is irreversibly extended, always in the same direction, beyond themselves.

We have only to think for a moment to realise that such a process of synthesis cannot be continued to its limit without causing the appearance, at the term of the universal drift, and in conformity with the law of complexity, of some centre— and it must be a super-personal and super-personalising centre in which all the reflective atoms of the world will be finally assembled, super-centred and consolidated.

This proposition may seem very far-fetched; but the universe cannot *be thought of as fully meeting the requirements, both extrinsic and intrinsic, of anthropogenesis* unless it takes on the form of a convergent psychic milieu. It must necessarily reach its fulfilment, ahead of us, in some pole of super-consciousness in which all the personalised grains of consciousness survive and 'super-live'. It culminates in an *Omega Point*.

This is the hypothesis forced upon us by experience if we extend the lines of the Phenomenon of Man to their natural limit.

Let us now completely reverse the perspective: by that I mean that after trying to advance from the bottom to the top along the experimental roads opened up by science, let us look at things from the top downwards, starting from the peaks to which we are raised by Christianity and religion.

II. THE SUPER-CHRIST

By Super-Christ I most certainly do not mean *another* Christ, a second Christ different from and greater than the first. I mean *the same* Christ, the Christ of all time, revealing himself to us in a form and in dimensions, with an urgency and area of contact, that are enlarged and given new force.

We can readily appreciate that the appearance in Christian consciousness of a Christ so magnified will immediately result in the appearance in human consciousness of Super-humanity.

'Apparuit humanitas.' Both in nature and in function, Christ gathers up in himself and consummates the totality and the fulness of humanity. On that point, all believers are unanimous. If, in consequence, the evidence obliges our reason (as we have just seen) to accept that something greater than the man of today is in gestation on earth, it means that in order to be able to continue to worship as before we must be able to say to ourselves, as we look at the Son of man, 'Apparuit Super-humanitas'.

Christ coincides (though this assertion will have to be examined more deeply) with what I earlier called Omega Point.

Christ, therefore, possesses all the super-human attributes of Omega Point.

Those two propositions, to my mind, sum up the passionate expectations contained in our Christology and express the progress it is already effecting.

A. CHRIST-OMEGA

We may dig things over as much as we please, but the universe cannot have two heads—it cannot be 'bicephalic'. However supernatural, therefore, the synthesising operation attributed by dogma to the Incarnate Word may ultimately be, it cannot be effected in a divergence from the natural convergence of the world, as defined above. The universal Christic centre, determined by theology, and the universal cosmic centre postulated by anthropogenesis: these two focal points ultimately coincide (or at least overlap) in the historical setting in which we are contained. Christ would not be the sole Mover, the sole Issue, of the universe if it were possible for the universe in any way to integrate itself, even to a lesser degree, apart from Christ. And even more certainly, Christ, it would seem, would have been physically incapable of supernaturally centering the universe upon himself if it had not provided the Incarnation with a specially favoured point at which, in virtue of their natural structure, all the strands of the cosmos tend to meet together. It is therefore towards Christ, in fact, that we turn our eyes when, however approximate our concept of it may be, we look ahead towards a higher pole of humanisation and personalisation.

In position and function, Christ, here and now, fills for us the place of Omega Point.

Let us consider what are the theoretical and practical consequences, for our minds and hearts, of this identification.

B. CHRIST THE EVOLVER

In spite of the repeated assertions of St Paul and the Greek Fathers, Christ's universal power over Creation has hitherto been considered by theologians primarily in an extrinsic and juridical aspect. 'Christ is King of the world, because his

165

Father *declared* him to be King. He is master of all because all has been given to him.' That is about as far as the teachers in Israel went, or were prepared to venture, in their explanations of the dogma. Except in regard to the mysterious 'sanctifying grace', the organic side of the Incarnation, and in consequence its physical presuppositions or conditions, were relegated to the background: the more readily so, in that the recent and terrifying increased dimensions of our universe (in volume, duration, and number) seemed finally to make physical control of the cosmic totality by the Person Christ, inconceivable.

All these improbabilities disappear and St Paul's boldest sayings readily take on a literal meaning as soon as the world is seen to be suspended, by its conscious side, from an Omega Point of convergence, and Christ, in virtue of his Incarnation, is recognised as carrying out precisely the functions of Omega.

If Christ does indeed hold the position of Omega in the heaven of our universe (and this is perfectly possible, since, structurally, Omega is super-personal in nature) then a whole series of remarkable properties become the prerogative of his risen humanity.

In the first place, he is physically and literally, *He who fills all things*: at no instant in the world, is there any element of the world that has moved, that moves, that ever shall move, outside the directing flood he pours into them. Space and duration are filled by him.

Again physically and literally, he is he who *consummates*: the plenitude of the world being finally effected only in the final synthesis in which a supreme consciousness will appear upon total, supremely organised, complexity. And since he, Christ, is the organic principle of this harmonising process, the whole universe is *ipso facto* stamped with his character, shaped according to his direction, and animated by his form.

Finally, and once more physically and literally, since all the structural lines of the world converge upon him and are knitted together in him, it is he who *gives its consistence* to the entire edifice of matter and Spirit. In him too, '*the head of Creation*', it follows, the fundamental cosmic process of cephalisation culminates and is completed, on a scale that is universal and with a depth that is supernatural, and yet in harmony with the whole of the past.

We see, then, that there is indeed no exaggeration in using the term Super-Christ to express that excess of greatness assumed in our consciousness by the Person of Christ in step with the awakening of our minds to the super-dimensions of the world and of mankind.

It is not, I insist, another Christ: it is the same Christ, still and always the same, and even more so in that it is precisely in order to retain for him his essential property of being *co-extensive with the world* that we are obliged to make him undergo this colossal magnification.

Christ-Omega: the Christ, therefore, who animates and gathers up all the biological and spiritual energies developed by the universe. Finally, then, Christ the evolver.

It is in that form then, now clearly defined and all-embracing, that Christ the Redeemer and Saviour henceforth offers himself for our worship.

III. SUPER-CHARITY

To say that Christ is the term and motive force of evolution, to say that he manifests himself as 'evolver', is implicitly to recognise that he becomes attainable in and through the whole process of evolution. Let us examine the consequences for our interior life of this amazing situation.

There are three, and they may be expressed as follows: 'Under the influence of the Super-Christ, our charity is universalised, becomes dynamic and is synthesised.'

167

Let us look at each of the terms of this threefold transformation in turn.

1. *First, our charity is universalised.* By definition, the Christian is, and always has been, the man who loves God, and his neighbour as himself. But has not this love necessarily remained hitherto particularist and extrinsic in its explicit realisation? For many who believe, Christ is still the mysterious personage who after having passed through history two thousand years ago now reigns in a Heaven that is divorced from earth; and our neighbour is still a swarm of human individuals, multiplied with no recognisable rule nor reason, and associated together by the arbitrary force of laws and conventions. In such a view there is little or even no place for the immensities of sidereal or living matter, for the multitude of the world's natural elements and events, for the impressive unfolding of cosmic processes.

Now, it is precisely this pluralism, emotionally so confusing, which vanishes under the rays of the Super-Christ, to make way for a warm and resplendent unity.

Since, in fact, everything in the universe ultimately proceeds towards Christ-Omega; since the whole of cosmogenesis is ultimately, through anthropogenesis, expressed in a Christogenesis; it follows that, in the integral totality of its tangible strata, the real is charged with a divine Presence. As the mystics felt instinctively, everything becomes physically and literally lovable in God; and God, in return, becomes intelligible and lovable in everything around us. In the breadth and depth of its cosmic stuff, in the bewildering number of the elements and events that make it up, and in the wide sweep, too, of the overall currents that dominate it and carry it along as one single great river, the world, filled by God, appears to our enlightened eyes as simply a setting in which universal communion can be attained, and a concrete expression of that communion.

2. *Secondly, our charity becomes dynamic.* Hitherto, to love God and one's neighbour might have seemed no more than an attitude of contemplation and compassion. Was not to love God to rise above human distractions and passions in order to find rest in the light and unvarying warmth of the divine Sun? And was not to love one's neighbour primarily to bind up the wounds of one's fellow men and alleviate their suffering? Detachment and pity—escape from the world and mitigation of evil—in the eyes of the Gentiles could not those two notes be legitimately regarded as the Christian characteristics of charity?

Here again we find a complete change: our whole outlook widens and is vitalised to the scale of the universalised Christ.

If, let me repeat, the whole progress of the world does indeed conform to a Christogenesis (or, which comes to the same thing, if Christ can be fully attained only at the term and peak of cosmic evolution), then it is abundantly clear that we can make our way towards him and apprehend him only in the effort to complete and synthesise everything in him. In consequence, it is the general ascent of life towards fuller consciousness, it is man's effort in its entirety, that are now organically and with full justification once more included among the things with which charity is concerned and which it hopes to achieve. If we are to love the Super-Christ we must at all costs see to it that the universe and mankind push ahead, in us and in each of our co-elements—in particular in the other 'grains of thought', our fellow-men.

To co-operate in total cosmic evolution is the only deliberate act that can adequately express our devotion to an evolutive and universal Christ.

3. *By that very fact, our charity is synthesised.* At first that expression may seem obscure, and it should be explained.

In the detail, and on the scale of 'ordinary' life, much that we do is independent of love. To love (between 'persons') is to be drawn together and brought closer *centre-to-centre*. In our lives, this 'centric' condition is seldom achieved. It may be that we are dealing with objects (material, infra-living, or intellectual) which are by their nature non-centred and impersonal; it may be that in our human inter-relationships we come into contact with our fellows only 'tangentially', through our interests, through our functions, or for business dealings—in either case, we are generally working, or seeking, enjoying ourselves or suffering, without loving—without even suspecting that it is possible for us to love—the thing or person with which we are concerned. Thus our interior life remains fragmented and pluralised.

Consider, on the other hand, what happens if above (or rather at the heart of) this plurality there rises the central reality of Christ the evolver. In virtue of his position as the Omega of the world, Christ, we have seen, represents the focus point towards which and in which all things *converge*. In other words, he appears as a Person with whom all reality (provided we understand that in the appropriate positive sense) effects an approach and a contact in the only direction that is possible: *the line in which their centres lie*.

This can mean but one thing, that every operation, once it is directed towards him, assumes, without any change of its own nature, the psychical character of a centre-to-centre relationship, in other words, of an act of love.

Eating, drinking, working, seeking; creating truth or beauty or happiness; all these things could, until now, have seemed to us heterogeneous, disparate, activities, incapable of being reduced to terms of one another—loving being no more than one of a number of branches in this divergent psychical efflorescence.

Now, however, that it is directed towards the Super-Christ, the fascicle draws itself together. Like the countless shades that combine in nature to produce a single white light, so the infinite modalities of action are fused, without being confused, in one single colour under the mighty power of the universal Christ; and it is love that heads this movement: love, not simply the common factor through which the multiplicity of human activities attains its cohesion, but love, *the higher, universal, and synthesised form of spiritual energy*, in which all the other energies of the soul are transformed and sublimated, once they fall within 'the field of Omega'.

Originally, the Christian had no desire except to be able to love, at all times and whatever he was doing, *at the same time as he was acting*. Now he sees that he can love *by his activity*, in other words he can directly be united to the divine centre by his every action, no matter what form it may take.

In that centre every activity, if I may use the phrase, is 'amorised'.

How could it be otherwise, if the universe is to maintain its equilibrium?

A Super-mankind calls for a Super-Christ.

A Super-Christ calls for a *Super-charity*.

COHERENCE, ACTIVANCE,[5] TRUTH

When drawing attention earlier to the rising of Super-mankind over our horizon, I noted that the new dawn makes itself felt in our consciousness by a sense of, and a more explicit demand for, the irreversibility of spirit. This study would be incomplete if I did not now point out a similar and even more marked phenomenon: that by which the Super-Christ, as he

[5] By activance (activating potential) I mean the power an intellectual or mystical outlook possesses of developing spiritual energies in us and super-stimulating them.

emerges, pre-acts upon our hearts too in a way that can be recorded—and precisely by arousing them to the act of Super-charity.

When, a moment ago, I was describing the nature and attributes of this supreme virtue, the reader may have thought that all I was doing was to develop, in the abstract and for a distant future (taking them, moreover, to their extreme limit), the logical consequences for our interior life of faith in a universal Christ. It was, in fact, in very really concrete terms and with an eye on the present that I meant what I said. At this moment there are men, many men, who by making the conjunction of the two ideas of Incarnation and evolution a real element in their lives, are succeeding in effecting the synthesis of the personal and the universal. For the first time in history men have become capable not only of knowing and serving evolution but of *loving it*; thus they are beginning to be able to say to God, explicitly, as a matter of habit and effortlessly, that they love him not only with their whole heart and their whole soul, but 'with the whole universe'.

I should like, in concluding, to make you realise the importance of this psychological event, taken simply in itself as a pure fact of experience.

In a general way, we have seen, we may say that, considered in that portion of it which is ascending, the universe drifts towards, and integrates itself, in the direction in which organic complexity is the most advanced. To this we must add, that in the same process it directs itself to those areas and that state in which activity is constantly heightened.

These are the two fundamental laws of 'psycho-dynamics'.

We now see the way in which Super-charity, in view of its nature, presents itself to us: from the point of view of 'complexity', as a complete totalisation; and from the point of view of dynamics, as an intensification to the maximum of all possible forms of conscious activity—and this because in Super-charity everything becomes love, and because love is the most intense form that spiritual energy can take.

If we combine these two groups of propositions, two conclusions automatically result.

The first is that with the awakening of Super-charity on earth, the first manifestations make themselves felt of a transformation that is destined progressively to extend to the whole Noosphere and so bring it to its final state of equilibrium.

And the second is that the two combined principles of coherence and activating potential whose influence, and *only* whose influence, makes Super-charity possible, are no fantasy or dream: their fruit is proof that they bear an infallible stamp of objectivity and truth.

Peking, August 1943

CHAPTER XI

ACTION AND ACTIVATION

---

1. *The principle of the maximum : its general form*

In man's thought the problem of knowledge is gradually tending to be linked with, even perhaps to be subordinated to, the problem of action. For the ancient philosophers 'to be' was above all 'to know'. For modern philosophers, 'to be' is coming to be synonymous with 'to grow' and 'to become'. We are witnessing the entry, not only into physics but into metaphysics too, of a dynamism.

The purpose of this note is not to analyse the causes of this phenomenon and the process it follows, nor to distinguish its possible term. I have the more simple and more practical aim of trying to find out, and helping the reader to see, where the principles of a philosophy of action will take us if they are followed up in their full rigour.

From the standpoint of a metaphysics of vision, the postulate implicitly accepted was that the real has the property of being fully and indefinitely *intelligible* to our reason. Similarly, from the point of view of action, the fundamental, even if unacknowledged, presupposition behind our intellectual approach is, I think it will be admitted, that in relation to our will the real must, again, be, to the highest possible degree and with no limit, *actable* and *activating*. In other words, there would be a contradiction, an ontological imbalance, in the world if our capacity to desire and to act were found to be greater, even in one single point, than the possibilities offered to us by our cosmic environment.

The more one thinks along these lines, the stronger grows

one's conviction that in practice the first and essential condition of reality imposed on the universal object by the human subject we represent is that it must contain a *maximum* not only of truth but of magnetic power: not an absolute maximum, a maximum *in se*, as in Leibniz's type of optimism (if, indeed, that has any meaning) but a relative maximum in relation to our capacities and aspirations for understanding and creating.

'By an organic and metaphysical necessity, the world cannot fall short, in coherence or in value, of the ultimate demands of our reason and our hearts.' Or, to put it positively: 'What our reason and our hearts essentially and positively demand, if they are to be satisfied, that the world possesses.' Or again, 'What is the most intelligible and the most activating is necessarily the most real and the most true.'

Let us ignore for the moment the first term in this principle of the maximum (the term that relates to intelligibility) as being more familiar or less fruitful, and concentrate on the second half, which concerns action.

2. *The principle of maximum activance: primary consequences*

When restricted to the sphere of action, the principle of the maximum, we have just seen, means that if the universe is to be intrinsically reconcilable with the presence in it of our reflective will, it must do more than open up for us a field of positive action, of *unspecified* value. That field must, in addition, be such that the real is seen always to be capable of meeting our demand for fuller being, without ever falling short or being exhausted. In virtue of its structure the world must offer, in relation to our zest for action, a maximum power of stimulation (a maximum '*activance*)'. To be merely *actable*, it must be supremely *activating*.

175

When that proposition is accepted, it becomes evident that we hold a real instrument with which we can, if we wish, triangulate the universe around us by taking bearings on its highest peaks. Suppose, in fact, that we should succeed, by reflecting upon ourselves, in determining a certain number of major properties the lack of which would, in our eyes, clearly rob the world of an important (or, still more, a vital) part of its power of activance. We would then, in virtue of our postulate, be justified in saying that those properties belong to the world really and objectively. Within these limits and at this level, the law of our ambitions becomes the law of the objective world.

The whole question, then, is whether such properties exist. I am convinced that they do, and that they are even more numerous than we would at first believe. And, to my mind, it is precisely here, in this rich store of clearly *defined* demands that the philosophy of action has the edge, from the point of view of analysing the real, over the philosophy of the pure intelligible.

Put it to the experimental test. Let us watch ourselves acting, and try to isolate, at the inmost core of our action, the basic milieu within which each individual motive and impulse is born and by which it is sustained. We shall very soon distinguish three general conditions imposed on the universe (each corresponding to a kind of maximum): if these are not satisfied —if a single one is not—forthwith our hands, when it comes to action, are tied, our wings are clipped.

a. In the first place, if it is not to disappoint and dishearten our effort, the world must be and must remain *open*. By this I mean that, to satisfy us, Nature must continually represent for us a reservoir of discoveries from which we can at every moment expect something completely new to emerge. It must be a spring that never dries up, and at the same time an ever plastic wax, that can indefinitely be remodelled or re-cast by our hands.

b. Secondly, as the world advances, it must be *irreversible*. At a first stage, this means no more than that if it is to have real value for us, each new step we take must bring with it a permanent gain—it must mark one more rung in the ladder of our ascent. But this is not all. At a second stage, a more radical demand underlies this first requirement of our will. That the general gradient of our evolution be positive, that our conquests, taken as a whole, be cumulative: this in itself means a great deal but it would still be quite useless, if we had reason to fear that we might one day have to come down from the peak to which this evolution is leading us. In a more literal sense than the worthy Thucydides could have hoped for his history, man, in his internal mechanism, is so constructed that he cannot be set in motion except under the magnetic attraction of a *ktêma eis aei*, of a treasure that will never perish. This is the fact, as old and familiar in its roots as human consciousness, to define whose immense scope, nevertheless, called for the modern psycho-philosophy of action.

c. Thirdly, the world, considered from the point of view of the fruit it is quietly ripening at the heart of its genesis, must contain, or must be preparing, something that is unique and indispensable to the plenitude of the real. In a form that will have to be precisely determined in accordance with the demands of metaphysics, cosmic evolution must (if it is not to lose all its power to attract us) effect through us a work of *absolute value*.

An open world—an irreversible world—a world of absolute value: the only type of world in which our delight in action can be complete.

If anyone should happen to raise the objection that, so far as

177

he is concerned, he does not experience the need, *if he is to be able to act*, of such far-reaching support, I shall answer that he cannot perhaps read the secrets of his own heart—or, again, that perhaps he is not yet fully alive to what constitutes the soul of his own time; for, in spite of our immobilist illusions, human consciousness changes and grows richer with the centuries. Both in the species and in the individual certain symptoms and certain aspirations appear only with age. Only a minority, maybe, is beginning as yet to formulate for itself the three demands I have just noted, the three preliminary conditions imposed on the universe by our freedom before it consents to embrace its evolution. But of that minority we may already say that it is at this moment opening the breach through which we shall all pass tomorrow. And it is to those pioneers that I am speaking.

3. *The principle of maximum activance: secondary consequences*

We may, then, leave aside any further discussion either of the general validity of the principle of maximum activance, or of the legitimacy of the three primary consequences we have just derived from it: let us, instead, take a further step and try to see whether perhaps certain fundamental modifications must not be made in our customary ways of thinking, as soon as we finally decide that logically and without reservation, we can be at home only in a universe that is open, irreversible and endowed with an absolute quality.

a. First, the world is open, and must remain so. It may happen that in some of its elements, in some of its lower reaches, it begins to run dry as we continue our investigations, as though the source was silting up: even so, we can be certain that in its

178

peaks and as a whole, it still remains an inexhaustible source of renewal and growth. This means that all moral teaching, all philosophy, and all theology (even 'revealed' theology) are *a priori* suspect, and even condemned, the moment that, and to the extent that, they claim to draw a *closed circle* around our powers of rejuvenation and discovery. The more successful a synthesis and the more true an idea, the wider and the more unforeseen are the horizons they open up to our inquiry. Is it not the poison of *closed* orthodoxies that kills one philosophical system after another and offers the most serious threat to the life of religions?

b. Secondly, the world is irreversible, which means that, considered in its evolutionary essence, it is imperishable. Life-prisoners on a planet whose days are numbered, we take the easy way out, in order to dull the threat that hangs heavy on us, of postponing its realisation to a date that is distant and, above all, *indeterminate.* Tactics, however, that are more or less valid in the case of our individual lives, are no more than an infantile gesture where the universe is concerned. No: unless it is going to disappoint us radically, the conscious universe *cannot* die absolutely. Total death and reflective activity are cosmically incompatible. There can be no way of avoiding that conclusion. This can mean only one thing: that if our action is to break through the magic circle of entropy—the scientific karma that seems as though it must inexorably pull us back into unconsciousness with the whole mass of the nebulae and the multitudes of stars—then, with all the strength at its command, it must find some tangent along which to escape, and a transcendent fixed point to which it can cling, outside the phenomenon. As we might well expect, the problem of the Prime Mover and an ultimate Gatherer ahead loses none of its gravity: on the contrary it increases in importance and urgency with the formidably increased dimensions science

179

imposes on our conceptions of the universe. It is not only in the thought of philosophers or the contemplation of mystics—but in the general consciousness of man—that the awareness of some divine presence underlying evolution demands to be clearly recognised as an ultimate and constant support for action.

c. Finally, in its genesis the world is maturing something that is absolute. Here, once again, we clash, and this time even more violently, with the antinom by which human reason has always been pulled up short when it tries to link together unity and plurality within the universe. Since God cannot be conceived except as monopolising in himself the totality of being— then either the world is no more than appearance—or else it is in itself a part, an aspect, or a phase of God. To escape from this dilemma Christian metaphysics has developed its notion of *participated being*, a lower or secondary form of being ('sub-being' one might say) gratuitously drawn from 'non-being' by a special act of transcendent causality, 'creatio ex nihilo'. I have no intention of contesting this idea of an ontological distinction between the divine Centre and the elementary centres that form the world. It is essential, as we shall see later, if we are to respect the mystical requirements of a supremely 'communicating' universe. Nevertheless, from the point of view of action, I shall note that the Christian solution,[1] if it is not taken further that it actually goes, is certainly unable to fulfil the conditions of activance imposed on the universe by the progress of modern thought. An entirely gratuitous creation, a gesture of pure benevolence, with no other object, for the absolute Being, than to *share* his plenitude with a *corona* of participants of whom he has strictly no need—that

[1] The solution, that is, provided by a theology that, from having failed properly to understand that, like all human knowledge, it must accept unpredictable developments, had prematurely determined its own limits. (Ed.)

could satisfy minds that had not yet awoken to the immensity of space-time, the colossal stores of energy and the unfathomable organic articulation of the phenomenal world; but we who have become conscious (and vividly so) of the majesty, the implacability, and the truly 'divine' power of cosmic evolution—we would suffer deeply, in the honour we pay to being, and the respect we have for God would be insulted, if all this great array, with its huge burden of toil and trouble, were no more than a sort of game whose sole aim was to make us supremely happy. We can accept that by ourselves and in ourselves we are initially nothing, nothing to the ultimate depths of ourselves; what is even more, indeed, our love, if it is to be complete love (see below) positively requires this. But if we could not somehow consciously feel that we cannot 'be of service to God' without God adding something to himself, that would most certainly destroy, at the heart of our freedom, the intimate driving forces of action. To be happy? But what use have we for the *selfish* happiness of *sharing* the joy of the supreme Being, when we can dream of the infinitely greater happiness of completing that joy?[2] And, however gratuitous we may suppose Creation 'ex nihilo' to be, is it not inevitably marked in the first place (whatever the theoreticians of 'participated being' may have said) by an absolute increase of unification, and therefore of *unity*, in the pleromised real?

I have neither the authority nor the competence to decide at what precise point one should apply the 'transposition of concepts' necessary to justify the ambitions newly emerging in the heart of man, now that he has become conscious of the

---

[2] The problem of participated being has always been a philosophical problem of extreme difficulty. In 1926, Père Teilhard, carrying as far as possible his interpretation of the Johannine and Pauline texts, wrote, 'Owing to the interrelation between matter, soul and Christ . . . with each one of our *works*, we labour—in individual separation, but no less really—to build the Pleroma; that is to say, we bring to Christ a little fulfilment' (*Le Milieu Divin*, p. 34, Fontana, p. 62). (Ed.)

181

true dimensions, and therefore the true value, of his universe. All I can say is that if this transformation is to retain the value of the world without affecting God, it must go deep and reach the very core of our ontology. Philosophically we are still living in an antiquated body of thought, governed by the notions of immobility and substance. These two key notions, vaguely founded and modelled upon sensorial evidence that at one time could be regarded as perennial and safe from attack, are now, we must admit, being undermined by a physics that is succeeding in abolishing any real distinction, for our reason, between extension and motion, between particles and waves, between matter and light, between space and time . . . Under the pressure and contagious influence of these revolutionary re-appraisals (whose result is in every case to bring out a necessary link between pairs of realities that hitherto seemed to us as independent as they possibly could be), we are inevitably making our way to a completely new concept of *being*: in this the hitherto contradictory attributes of the '*ens ab alio*' and the '*ens a se*', of the world and God, would be combined in a general synthetic function (cf. algebraic functions including an imaginary term): God completely other in nature than the world and yet unable to dispense with it.[3]

4. Action and union

Understanding and will, intelligence and action: these two key faculties of the mind meet in depth (or, more precisely, in height) in a single radical need, of which they are derivations, aspects or modes: the need to unify. Whether we consider the

[3] What I have in mind here is a synthetic re-definition of being, which, taken in its most general form, would include, *both simultaneously*, an absolute term and a participated term. What makes the God-world antinomy insoluble is that we first split up a natural pair and then persist in considering the two terms *in succession*.

work of reason in its efforts to synthesise, or that of the will in what it constructs (or rejects), the basic impulse is the same—to introduce order and organisation into the multiple, to suppress plurality in and around ourselves. Once this point is understood, it becomes clear that the principle of the maximum can be expressed in an even more general form than that which we first gave it. If there is to be complete coherence between our consciousness and the universe (in other words, if the real is to possess, as we demand, a maximum of intelligibility and activance), then we must ultimately be able to see that it is supremely *communicating*. This can only mean that of all the ways in which we try to picture the world, that one alone is real which most completely satisfies our thirst for unity.

Granting that, is it possible, as it is in the case of activance, to define a particular type of world, in which, by reason of its structure, the 'unity-potential' is greater than in any other world we could conceive or imagine? It is, provided we first make the necessary distinction and choice between two ways, often confused even though diametrically opposed, which have been tried out in turn by human mysticism in its age-old effort to make everything one: the way of simplification, and the way of synthesis.

a. If we follow the tendencies expressed in *the way of simplification* ('the Road of the East'), the one is found, 'reveals itself', by mere suppression of the multiple which hides it from us. Whether the world is pure illusion, or whether it is an ephemeral modality of absolute being, it must be dissipated and re-absorbed (and that is all that is needed) for God to appear: God, who ultimately exhausts in himself all possible consciousness. In this view, the elements of the world vanish as they come together with God. The process depersonalises and absorbs them. It is not, in fact, *union* but simply (and that is

183

putting it at the highest) *fusion*. The one, completely without structure, neither presupposes nor entails *any unification*.

b. On the other hand, according to those who follow *the way of synthesis* ('the new road of the West'), the one is constituted or is to be found only through organisation of the multiple, each element of which, therefore, when taken to its extreme limit, possesses the double essential property (1) of converging upon God, with all the other elements that surround it, and (2) of becoming more deeply centred upon itself, in the un-communicable, the more deeply it forms one with the divine centre of all convergence. In this view, as the elements lose themselves in God, so they complete themselves. Union differentiates its terms—it super-personalises them. There is, ultimately, *no unity, without unification.*

Unity of singularity, and unity of complexity.

Of these two contradictory concepts (of which each defines an ascetical and mystical system) the first, by definition, robs the world and its developments of all value. Its activance *is nil*. This we can accordingly dismiss out of hand. The second, on the contrary, stimulates and nourishes to a supreme degree our zest for action. This, then, is the right road and the true road. The only type of universe in which our mystical need for unity can legitimately flourish is undoubtedly that in which the evolution that embraces us takes the general form of a *divinising convergence*. If that is granted, what particular conditions, once again, must be satisfied by the world and God if this convergence (that is, this 'communion') is to reach its maximum in intimacy and intensity—subjective conditions in terms of requirements, objective, therefore, in terms of reality?

They can be reduced to three.

The first is that the world must remain and continue to become more fully conscious of itself, the more completely it is unified in God. For this reason, and in spite of their enticing appearance, 'constructive' monisms such as that of Spinoza are only a deceptive lure for the mind. In the first place they are, when all is said and done, unintelligible to the philosopher, since (and in this they resemble the negative monisms of the eastern type) they assume that union absorbs and fuses, whereas its nature is to differentiate. Secondly, they fail to satisfy the mystic, since all love becomes impossible within a divine substance that is strictly monocentric.

The second condition is, that the elements of the world be more fully in a condition of dependence on God, the more they acquire consciousness and consistence in him, through unification.

And the third is that the more these same elements find themselves dependent on God, the more at the same time shall they have the consciousness that, in certain regards, God could not (or at least can no longer) dispense with them.[4]

Here again, as we anticipated, we meet (formulated this time by mysticism) the same disconcerting demand that action had already voiced. If participated being is to act effectively, it must (though we still have to find a formula to express this) possess, *in its own way*, something that is absolute and non-contingent in its formation.[5] I said earlier that the solution of the antinomy may not be found until, under the influence of the new 'epistemology' introduced in our time by science, we overhaul the very foundations of our ontology. I would suggest here, more exactly, that what we at present lack in our confrontation with the new problems raised for us

[4] The explicit reservations Teilhard makes in laying down this third condition, should be noted: 'in certain regards . . . or at least can no longer'. If these reservations are accepted, it would not appear that the theory put forward here as a suggestion is incompatible with the traditional doctrine of God's free decision in the creative act. (Ed.)

[5] Is it not in as much as it is destined to constitute the mystical Body of Christ, in other words effectively to participate in his divinity, that participated being acquires 'something that is absolute and non-contingent'? (Ed.)

by the universe, is a general theory of the genetical relationship between *being, unity* and *unification. We need a metaphysics based on the creative function and maximalist demands of union.*[6]

Unpublished, Peking, 9 August 1945

[6] Would not the most general formula in which we could understand, foresee and forward the real, be simply to posit and define the real as a system subject to the single condition of effecting, *by way of unification, a maximum unity*? In such a system it would seem to be possible *to deduce* the existence of the cosmic, peripheral, multiple on the same ground as the fontal and focal triune unity of God.

CHAPTER XII

CATHOLICISM AND SCIENCE

The conflict between science and faith has not such paramount im-
portance for our contemporaries as that between the Church and the
Revolution. Nevertheless it is still a central problem, and we are glad
to see it treated by a great scientist who has earned our gratitude by
restoring to modern Christianity its sense of cosmology (. . .) Here is
what Père Teilhard de Chardin has to say: (from the review
Esprit).

It is always rash and taking too much upon oneself to speak in
the name of a group, if the group as a whole is as homogeneous
and vitally knit together as the Catholic Body. Rather, then,
than try to make a general diagnosis of the Church's attitude
to science, I shall confine myself, in answering *Esprit's* enquiry,
to pointing out the recent appearance inside the body of
Catholicism of a particularly lively and significant movement
which (if God spares it) may be regarded as bringing a radical
and constructive solution to the conflict that ever since the
Renaissance has constantly brought science and faith into
opposition.

First, let us examine the essential nature of this conflict.

During a first, and much the longest, phase, the hostility
between experience and Revelation was seen almost entirely
in local difficulties encountered by exegesis in its attempt to
reconcile Biblical statements with the results of observation:
the immobility of the earth, for example, and the seven days
of Creation. Gradually, however, with progress in physics and

187

natural sciences, a much more general and much deeper schism ultimately became apparent. By force of circumstances (in view of the date of its birth) the best that Christian dogma could do, originally, was to express itself in the dimensions and to the requirements of a universe that in many respects was still the Alexandrine cosmos: a universe harmoniously revolving upon itself, limited and divisible in extension and duration, made up of objects more or less arbitrarily transposable in space and time. At the time we are speaking of, this view, under the effort of human thought, was beginning to change. Space was becoming boundless. Time was being converted into organic duration. And within this vitalised domain the elements of the world were developing so close an interrelationship that the appearance of any one of them was inconceivable except as a function of the global history of the whole system. In man's eyes a universe *in genesis* was irresistibly taking the place of the static universe of the theologians. Inevitably again, a specific form of mysticism was emerging from this new intuition: faith, amounting practically to worship, in the terrestrial and cosmic future of evolution. Thus, from beneath exegetical difficulties in matters of detail, a fundamental religious antinomy ended by coming to the surface: the conflict that was involved (though this was not clearly realised) in the Galileo controversy. With the universe rescued from immobility, a kind of divinity, completely immanent in the world, was progressively tending to take the place in man's consciousness of the transcendent Christian God.

That was the fatal danger whose threat to the Catholic faith, in our era, was daily becoming more serious.

It is, then, at this critical point of a conflict which has now reached its full dimensions that the reaction of believers is beginning to crystallise. Hitherto, in their confrontation with the scientific neo-gospel, Catholics had simply remained on the defensive. Their over-all strategy was confined to showing that in spite of every new discovery their position was still tenable; to admit (if the worst came to the worst) that evolution was a plausible but nevertheless precarious hypothesis. Why did they show such timidity? I said earlier that Christian dogma, as it first emerged, had necessarily adapted itself to a cosmos of the static type. It could not do otherwise, because at that time human reason could not conceive the world in any other form. But consider what would happen if an attempt were made, following a line already suggested by the Greek Fathers long ago, to transpose the evidence of Revelation into a universe of the non-static type. It is to this that in our time a number (an ever-increasing number, I may say) of Catholic thinkers have turned their attention; and we have not had long to wait for the results of their attempt. Experience shows that traditional Christology can accept an evolutionary world-structure; but, what is even more, and what contradicts all predictions, it is within this new organic and unitary ambience, and by reason of this particular curve of linked Space-Time, that it can develop most freely and fully. It is there that Christology takes on its true form. The great cosmic attributes of Christ, those (more particularly in St Paul and St John) which accord to him a universal and final primacy over Creation—these had without difficulty been susceptible of a moral and juridical explanation. But it is only in the setting of an evolution that they take on their full dimensions: always subject to a condition which science itself in fact suggests in so far as it makes up its mind to allow man his rightful place in Nature—that this evolution be of the type that is both spiritual and convergent. With that reservation nothing is simpler or more tempting than to look to revealed Christogenesis for an ultimate explanation of the Cosmogenesis of the scientists and to set the final seal upon it. Christianity and evolution: not two irreconcilable points of view, but two ways of looking at things that are designed to dovetail together, each completing the other. After all, has not this alliance for long been deeply enshrined in the instinctive felicity of the spoken language? Creation, Incarnation, Redemption—do not these very words, in their grammatical form, evoke the idea of a process rather than a local or instantaneous act?

Thus it is, I believe, that the incorporation and assimilation by Christian thought of modern evolutionary views is sufficient to break down the barrier that for four centuries has continually been rising between reason and faith. Once the immobilist obstacle has been removed there is nothing in future to prevent Catholics and non-Catholics from advancing together, hand in hand, along the highways of discovery. Today frank collaboration on both sides has become possible.

If, however, we ask whether all cause of divergence between yesterday's antagonists has been permanently removed we shall have to answer that it has not. Underlying the devotion to research which is common to both and identical in both, two contradictory mystical attitudes, two different 'spirits', can still be distinguished; and these are bound still, and for a long time to come, to find themselves in conflict. On one side there is the 'Faustian spirit' which attributes the secret of our destiny to a certain power inherent in mankind of fulfilling itself by its own energies, unaided; on the other side, the 'Christian spirit' whose tension, in its constructive effect, is towards union with a God who supports us and draws us to him through all the forces of a world in evolution.

Between these two spirits the ancient antagonism between science and religion is clearly re-appearing in an essential and subtle form; but by its very nature there is no longer anything sterile nor shameful in this new conflict. The old opposition between mobilists and immobilists has gone. Henceforth Catholics and non-Catholics meet as one through their basic faith in a progress of the earth. The whole problem between

190

the two consists in knowing which will perceive and attain the higher peak.

In this noble rivalry, pure scientists seem on the whole still to favour the Faustian spirit; but the Christian already has no fundamental doubt but that he will have the last word. For, ultimately, only his 'Christic' vision of the world is capable of providing man's effort with two elements without which our action cannot continue its forward progress to the very end:

1. valorisation
2. amorisation

First, a divine guarantee that, in spite of all death, the fruit of our labour is *irreversible* and *cannot be lost*.

Secondly, the magnetic attraction of an objective that is capable, *because its nature is super-personal*, of releasing deep in our souls the forces of love, beside which other forms of spiritual energy fade into insignificance and are as nothing.

Evolution is the daughter of science; but when all is said and done, it may well, perhaps, be faith in Christ that tomorrow will preserve in us the zest for evolution.

From 'Esprit', in a section entitled 'Face aux Valeurs modernes'
Paris, August 1946

CHAPTER XIII

DEGREES OF SCIENTIFIC CERTAINTY
IN THE IDEA OF EVOLUTION

For the last hundred years, through a breach opened by the natural sciences, the idea of evolution has infiltrated into human consciousness to such a degree that it permeates the whole extent of the experiential field of knowledge. It is interesting, accordingly, to consider just how deeply it has really penetrated into our minds, to what extent, that is, the prospects it opens up can henceforth be regarded as definitively incorporated in science.

From this point of view, it seems to me that we should distinguish three meanings (or degrees) in the notion of evolution. They may be expressed as follows, in decreasing order of general applicability and certainty.

1. At a first and completely general degree, the scientific idea of evolution implies no more than the affirmation of this fact: that every object and every event in the world has an antecedent which conditions its appearance among other phenomena. Nothing, we say, appears in history except by way of birth: so that each element in the universe is, by something in itself, a link in an unbreakable chain that stretches behind and in front of it until it is lost to view. This does not, of course, rule out the interpolation between two successive links, of a mutation, a jump, a critical point of emergence. It means, however, that everything we perceive has necessarily something ahead of it in time as well as something beside it in space—so much so that the totality of things taken as a whole forms a sort of network from which our experience can in no

192

way escape, and within which objects (the knots in the net) cannot be arbitrarily transposed.

At this degree of generality, at which evolution simply means the *organicity* of the stuff of the universe (a temporal, combined with a spatial, organicity) it is not enough, I must emphasise, to speak of certainty. What we should say is 'evidential fact'. For our age, to have become conscious of evolution means something very different from and much more than having discovered one further fact, however massive and important that fact may be. It means (as happens with a child when he acquires the sense of spatial depth) that we have become alive to a new *dimension*. The idea of evolution: not, as is still sometimes said, a mere hypothesis, but a condition of all experience—or again, if you prefer the expression, the universal curve to which all our present and future ways of constructing the universe must henceforth conform, if they are to be scientifically valid or even thinkable.

2. Now for a further step. Within an organic time-space system such as that within which, as I was saying, our scientific knowledge is contained, two general types of distribution can *a priori* be found: either disordered turbulence, or currents whose direction is controlled (whether statistically or towards a final end hardly matters). Here we leave the field of primordial dimensions to penetrate into that of observed facts. And what do the facts tell us?

In the present state of science, it would appear undeniable that (at least as a statistical effect) currents—*two* currents—can empirically be distinguished in the stuff of the cosmos: one, clearly universal, gradually taking matter back, by disintegration, towards an elementary physical energy of radiation; the other, local in its appearance, and coinciding with a sort of eddy of energy, in which matter, grouping itself in formidably complicated structures, takes the form of organic particles: in these a certain psychic interiority appears and grows greater

193

as a function of the complexity. There is a simultaneous drift towards complexity and towards consciousness: and that constitutes the whole phenomenon of life.

The relative importance and value of these two currents, of disintegration and aggregation, in the universe; their complementary character, necessary in different degrees for the cosmic structure; their final conditions of equilibrium—these are matters about which we may still be uncertain; but, so far as their existence is concerned, we can see them as something of which we can be definitively assured.

3. Let us now try to go even further, and this time consider more particularly the current of life. Taken as a whole, I said, during the six hundred million years or so that we are able to follow it, this current has, quite certainly, never ceased globally to rise in the direction of complexity-consciousness. Is it, however, still continuing to rise, and if so, is its behaviour divergent or convergent? and if the latter, where is it directing the axis of its course?

It is at this point, and only at this point, that we enter the still unsubstantiated field of hypothesis, that is to say of scientific thought in action. Starting from here, therefore, what I am going to say is *not yet* certain today. Still looking ahead into the future, I ask myself whether what we shall be certain about tomorrow, with regard to the exact form and future development of biological evolution (or even simply of evolution) will not depend essentially on the idea of the nature of *the human social phenomenon* that vigorously prosecuted scientific thought will enable us definitively to establish.

All around us mankind offers the remarkable spectacle of an ubiquitous zoological group whose branches instead of separating (as always happened hitherto in the animal species) fold back and involute upon themselves, developing at the same time a mechanical equipment and a psychism that are planetary in dimensions: this it clearly does under the influence of a type of *reflective* consciousness which establishes an intimate interconnexion of all the elements within the group. This massive fact still seems to us to be in no way unusual because we have got into the habit of looking on it as 'natural' or of disguising it under juridical formulas. If, on the other hand, we restore it to its place in the organic current of life, it immediately demands and *suggests* an explanation. In conformity with the law of complexity-consciousness, what, in fact, we are witnessing throughout the whole of human history is an ultra-synthesis directed towards grouping in some super-organism of a completely new type, not atoms, now, or molecules, or cells, but individuals and even complete phyla. In other words, mankind, in process of collectivisation around us, represents, I suggest, from the scientific point of view, the appearance in the universe of some super-complex.

Such a prospect may seem fantastic. Nevertheless, since it is completely logical, it is now being accepted as incontestable by an increasing number of serious thinkers—and with the consequence of supplying a possible answer to the very questions about the exact nature of evolution that were still undecided.

From this point of view, then:

a. It is clear, in the first place, that the vitalised portion of the world to which we belong has not yet stopped ascending towards the highest forms of complexity.

b. Secondly, it would appear that the seemingly divergent system of rays drawn by life in the course of its ascent entered, starting with man, an area in which it becomes convergent.

c. Finally, it would appear inevitable that if we are to conceive a term to this convergence, we must envisage somewhere ahead of us the emergence of *some peak*, corresponding to a general reflection upon themselves of the reflective elements of the earth: the formation of that peak, moreover, coinciding with a maximum of the demand for irreversibility that increases throughout the ages in the heart of man.

And when we finally reckon it up, this would mean that, for all its character of fragility and improbability, it is complexity (or at any rate consciousness, with which complexity goes hand in hand) that is destined in the universe ultimately to triumph over simplicity.

Here, I repeat, we are leaving behind the certain, but with the satisfaction of at last being confronted by the crucial point in the problem of evolution.

Proceedings of the International Philosophical Congress,
Rome, 15–20 November, 1946

CHAPTER XIV

ECUMENISM

At this moment a form of ecumenism is trying to assert itself: it is inevitably tied up with the psychic maturing of the earth, and therefore it will certainly come. About the conditions, however, in which this ecumenism can exist and take practical form, I am still uncertain—or rather it seems to me continually more evident that, as formulated at present (not, indeed in their basic aspiration, which is identical) the great mystical currents of today are not immediately reconcilable. In particular the eastern current (with its substratum-God in whom the elements and determinations of the world are dissolved as though within a sphere of infinite radius) seems to me to flow in the opposite direction from the western-Christian current (in which a God of tension and love is seen as the consummation of all personalisation and all determination, as the centre of universal concentration). Similarly, another fundamental psychological dualism seems to me to exist between Christians (or between representatives of various other groups) according to whether they accept or reject a certain faith in man at the root of their religious faith. Similarly again, two incompatible attitudes are apparent in the notion of a convergence of religions, so long as it is still not decided whether it must be effected between lines of equal value (syncretism) or along a privileged central axis—around a Christ who is incommensurable (in cosmic dignity) with any prophet or any Buddha (which is the only possible Christian and biological concept).

The three fundamental options (margin annotation)

In these conditions, I wonder whether the only two effective ways to ecumenism today may not be:

(summit-ecumenism) 1, between Christians, concerned to bring out an ultra-orthodox and ultra-human Christianity, on a truly 'cosmic' scale.

(basal-ecumenism) 2, between men in general, concerned to define and extend the foundations of a common human 'faith' in the future of mankind.

Combined, these two efforts would automatically lead us to the ecumenism we are waiting for; because faith in mankind, if carried as far as it can be taken, cannot, it would seem, be satisfied without a fully explicit Christ. Any other method, I fear, would lead to a failure to distinguish confusion from coherence, or to syncretisms without vigour or originality. What, in short, we need to achieve unity is the clear perception of a sharply defined (and real) 'type' of God, and an equally sharply defined 'type' of humanity.—If each group retains *its own* type of God and *its own* type of humanity (and if those types are heterogeneous) then no agreement can have serious value: it will be based only on ambiguities or pure sentimentality.

In these circumstances, a movement towards unity or an alliance between ecumenic movements that still retain these corrupting elements, would appear to me (apart from a general sympathy) still premature.

N.B. The options are not independent of one another. For example, to choose faith in man entails choosing the God of tension (and vice versa), and, in all probability, a universe that is cephalised (around a Christic nucleus).

Paris, 15 December 1946

CHAPTER XV

THE RELIGIOUS VALUE OF RESEARCH

In a recent letter our Fr General placed research (scientific research, and, more generally, research in every field of thought) at the head of the lines of advance and attack that he suggested to members of the Society. In this connexion I would like to offer and submit to your judgment a number of observations —from a somewhat special but, I think well-founded point of view—that confirm the lead we have just received from Rome.

1. A first point to note is the central importance in human occupations and preoccupations assumed by research during the last century and a half. Both historical research, which sets out to reconstruct the phases through which the world has travelled in the past—its trajectory; and experimental research, concentrated on the effort to analyse the present structure of the universe, and on the hope of gaining control of the movement that carries us along—in both these quarters, think of the zeal and fervour we can see on all sides! It is not so long ago that those who conducted such investigations were oddities, or idle dreamers—there were not many of them, in fact, and they were generally regarded as out of the ordinary, as 'characters'. Today it is millions of men who are so engaged, in all fields, and they are 'organised millions'. In the number of people employed, in the amount of money devoted to it, in the quantity of energy used, research is coming more and more to be the thing that really matters in the world. From being a private indulgence and a diversion it has already attained the rank and dignity of a vital human function—as vital, undoubtedly, as nutrition and reproduction.

Our age is often defined by the social rise of the masses. It could just as well (in fact, basically, the two phenomena are one) be characterised by the rise of research.

2. The modern rise of research—in itself the fact is undeniable: but how should we interpret it?

To my mind, there is only one possible explanation for the phenomenon; it is extremely simple in principle and at the same time extremely revolutionary in its consequences, and this is what it involves: we must make up our minds to accept, under the pressure of facts, that man is not yet complete in Nature, that he is not yet fully created—but that, in and around us, he is still in the full swing of evolution. In the first place, the human group, considered in its collective totality, is tending more and more distinctly to integrate itself organically in a super-reflective whole; seen correctly, this whole would indeed appear to be simply the direct continuation of the process in which, ever since the first origins of life, consciousness has continually been growing deeper through the emergence of progressively more complex organisms. That would appear to be the underlying significance of the great social phenomenon through which we are fighting our way. Secondly, under the operation of this collective super-reflection, the human mind is showing itself capable, here and now, of discovering and controlling the material sources of energy that in all probability will enable it (by direct action on the laws of reproduction, heredity and morphogenesis) to stimulate and influence at will— within certain limits we cannot yet foresee—the transformation of its own organism (including the brain . . .). That is the position we have reached at the moment.

From this point of view, then (and in all seriousness I believe that it has probability on its side), which means looking at things from the point of view of an evolution which, starting with man, rebounds reflectively upon itself, everything, I suggest, in the phenomenon I have just called 'the rise of re-search' becomes clarified and can be seen in its true perspective.

The passion or fever for knowledge and mastery which we are witnessing (or even sharing in) might in its origins have been mistaken for a mere crisis of curiosity, for no more than a feeling that we must explore that part of the universe which lies open to us. In fact, if (as we are beginning to suspect) the rise of life on earth has not indeed reached its term, the crisis is much more important and much more significant. For in that case, we must recognise, in the expansion and intensification of the effort to discover and invent we are making today, quite literally the emergence in the world of a new biological régime: that of evolution *in its hominised phase*. If research is engrossing human activity ever more completely, it is neither by whim, by fashion nor by chance; it is simply and solely that man has now become adult and finds himself irresistibly impelled to take control of the evolution of life on earth, and that research is the actual expression (at the reflective stage) of this evolutionary effort—an effort not simply to continue to exist, but to exist more fully; not simply to survive but irreversibly to 'super-live'.

3. And so, if I am not mistaken, we see in a flash of illumination, the answer to the question we started by asking: 'Why is it of such importance that we Jesuits should share so fully in man's research that we permeate and impregnate it with our faith and our love for Christ?' Why? Simply because (if what I have just been saying makes sense) in the Nature that surrounds us, research is the form in which the creative power of God is hidden and operates the most intensely. Through our research, new being, a further increase of consciousness, emerges in the world. This new creation would, surely, remain incomplete, 'unlivable', if it were not included as manifestly as possible—and, if possible, from birth—among the

201

forms assumed by an Incarnation and a Redemption, each a complement of the other. Every fruit of research is, by its nature, essentially, 'ontologically', Christifiable ('christifiabilis' and 'christificandus') so that the world may have complete existence in every part of it. The place for us priests, then, is precisely there, at the point from which all truth and all new power emerges: that so Christ may inform every growth, through man, of the universe in movement.

This is what one might call the 'theological' view of the question. Let us, if you will allow me, translate the same truth into terms of psychology and the interior life.

It is inevitable that under the influence of the almost magical powers that science gives him of controlling the progress of evolution, modern man should feel himself tied to the future, to the progress of the world, by a sort of religion which is often (wrongly, I believe) treated as neo-paganism. Faith in some evolutionary continuation of the world at variance with the gospel faith in a creative and personal God; a neo-humanist mysticism of an *Ahead* clashing with the Christian mysticism of the *Above*: in this apparent conflict between the old faith in a transcendent God and a youthful 'faith' in an immanent universe—it is precisely there, if I am not mistaken, that we shall find, *in its twofold form, scientific and social*, what is really essential in the modern religious crisis. Faith in God, and faith in man or in the world. The whole progress of the Kingdom of God, I am convinced, is today tied up with the problem of reconciling (not superficially but organically) these two currents. 'The problem of the two faiths'. What method should we follow in attacking it? And who should be given the task, the 'mission' of solving it?

In a first phase, it is clear, the work of the modern apologist (I am by no means fond of that word—it is too self-satisfied and makes too exclusive a claim to the truth—but I cannot think of a better one)—his work, anyway, must con-

202

sist in an effort of intellectual reflexion which will establish that the two faiths confronting one another (faith in God and faith in man) are not in opposition to one another: on the contrary, they represent the two essential components of a complete humano-Christian mysticism. There can be no truly live Christian faith if it does not reach and raise up, in its ascending movement, the totality of mankind's spiritual dynamism (the totality of the 'anima naturaliter christiana'.) Nor is faith in man psychologically possible if the evolutionary future of the world does not meet, in the transcendent, some focal point of irreversible personalisation. In short, it is impossible to rise Above without moving Ahead, or to progress Ahead without steering towards the Above. In the space of a single generation Christian thought, under the pressure of secular thought, has interpreted more profoundly the notions of Participation and Incarnation, and thus at the present moment has almost reached agreement on this point. This is not only a great comfort to the souls both of believers and non-believers, but also, undoubtedly, redounds to the greater glory of God. The importance of this first success cannot be overemphasised.

We must, however, be careful to note one thing: this dialectical demonstration that the 'two faiths' can be reconciled, brilliant though it is, will inevitably remain without fruit so long as it is not offered to the world as something lived in practice. That theoretically, *in abstracto*, the Above and the Ahead of the universe should coincide, is all to the good, and even counts for a great deal. But if the solution proposed is to be truly convincing and *communicate itself as such*, it still has to make itself unmistakably recognisable—it must prove itself, in act and in reality, that is *in vivo*. In other words if there is to emerge the resultant of the two forces (faith in God and faith in man) under whose impetus, I am convinced, Christianity is getting ready shortly to make a fresh leap forward (just as evolution is doing!)—then what we need is not treatises or books, but men who will serve as examples: men, I mean, who will be passionately and *simultaneously* animated in both types of faith and so effect in themselves, *in one heart*, the junction of the two mystical forces and display, to those they move among, the *realisation* of the synthesis. We need men who are all the more convinced of the sacred value of human effort in that they are primarily interested in God. Aerodynamic calculations had indeed been made before Blériot and the Wright brothers: but even so flying did not really begin to exist and become part of the economy of the earth until men actually took to the air.

So once again we come back to the importance of research work in the Society. Historically, because of the conditions of its birth and by its own family tradition, the Society has always been ready to defend and support Christian humanism. Formerly, almost the only way in which this instinctive sympathy could be expressed was in a somewhat superficial alliance between the humanities (or mathematics) and religion. Today, however, modern neo-humanism is no longer orientated towards the study and imitation of the great figures of the ancient world, but towards the genesis of some Superman; confronted with this, our traditional function in the Church takes on new gravity and responsibility. Every year, young men are arriving in our novitiates in whom (because they are of their own time) there shines and burns the flame of human faith in the future of mankind. Why do we delay in inculcating in them the duty (and giving them every possible opportunity) of feeding this fire and adding to its blaze from the very Fire they hope to find among us, the fire of the love of an incarnate God? Why are we not already launching them (with all the necessary precautions, of course) into the heart of human research?—not in those neutral or outdated zones in which progress is already slowing down (I have in mind the majority of the sciences of the past) but in those active and critical zones in which the fight is going on here and now to capture the great citadels of matter and life? To make *complete* believers, on both sides of the picture—is not that, for all its danger, our first mission?

In truth, if anyone can effect, as I was saying, *in actu et in vivo*, the essential synthesis of the two faiths that now confront one another in the world, surely by tradition and training, it is the sons of St Ignatius:—but with this condition—and it is an essential condition—that they have clearly grasped once and for all this fundamental truth, in which (if I am not deluding myself) is expressed the essence and the inescapable demands of 'the modern spirit'. This truth is that the Kingdom of Christ, to which our allegiance is sworn, cannot be established, either in battle or in peace, except upon an earth that has been taken, *along all the roads of technology and thought*, to the extreme limit of its humanisation.

I would be ready to accept, as a fair and complete summary of what I have been saying, the following sentence: and you may correct it yourselves, if you find it too crudely simplified.

'We priests, we Jesuits, must do more than interest ourselves and occupy ourselves in research. We must *believe* in it, because research (undertaken "with faith") is the very ground on which there may well be worked out the only humano-Christian mysticism that tomorrow can bring about the unanimity of man.'

Report presented by Père Teilhard during a study week organised by the Society of Jesus, Versailles, 20 August 1947

CHAPTER XVI

NOTE ON THE BIOLOGICAL STRUCTURE OF MANKIND

Practically all those (ethnographers, politicians, economists, moralists) who profess to study society and develop its structure, work as though social man were virgin wax in their hands, to be moulded at will: whereas in fact the living substance they are handling is biologically and historically characterised by a number of unmistakably defined lines of growth —sufficiently flexible to allow them to be used by the architects of the new earth, but sufficiently strong to nullify any attempt at arrangement that does not respect them.

I shall try in this note very briefly to enumerate, with their characteristics, these basic structural properties, with which everyone should be familiar. They may be reduced to three.

1. *The bifocal nature of every natural element of the cosmos*

In a general way, we may say that the behaviour, as we experience it, of each particulate cosmic element may be symbolised by an ellipse constructed on two foci of unequal and inconstant intensity: one (F_1) a focus of material arrangement, and the other (F_2) of psychism: F_2 (consciousness) appearing and growing initially as a function of F_1 (complexity), but soon showing a constant tendency to react constructively upon F_1, and so super-complexify it while itself becoming progressively more individualised. In pre-life (the area of infinitesimal complexities, atoms and molecules) F_2 is not perceptible, and is

therefore practically nil. In pre-human life (area of intermediate complexities), F_2 appears but still has only a slight influence on the growth of F_1, which is still mainly automatic.
Starting with man (the area of extremely great complexities),
F_2, now reflective, takes over to a large extent the function of
developing the progress of F_1 (by the play of invention) until,
as may be going to happen, the former loses all connexion
with the latter by achieving complete autonomy.[1]

This first characteristic of the stuff of the cosmos is a warning
to us that it would be completely useless to try to spiritualise
anything whatsoever in the universe around us without first
or at the same time developing its technical possibilities, and
vice-versa.

Let us try to examine the phenomenon more closely.

2. The organic value of the social phenomenon

Because we live immersed in the human mass, we are instinctively impelled to see in the process of social organisation
no more than an accidental and superficial association. The
more, however, we study its progressive nature and its psycho-
genic properties—properties, that is, that produce consciousness—the more certain it becomes that we were mistaken.
We have to recognise that, taken as a whole (the Noosphere),
mankind forms, or is in the process of developing, a vast
natural unit around our individual centres; being natural, it is
consequently bi-focal, and as such it obeys the general law of
complexity-consciousness analysed above. It has the advantage, too, that the phenomenon (since it takes place on our
own scale) is greatly magnified; its mechanism, therefore, becomes uncommonly easy to discern, and in it can be recognised the following chain of events:

[1] And by turning back upon what I have called elsewhere Omega Point.

a. Initially, an increasing planetary compression imposed on the human mass which (by multiplication) is rapidly spreading over the closed surface of the earth.

b. This produces a reaction, in the form of a similarly increasing organisation of the human mass, now forced to find a way of disposing itself that will reduce the planetary pressure (the formation of F1).

c. A corresponding collective intensification of consciousness, released by the arrangement of the human particles (rise of F2).

The whole process enables us to foresee, without any uncertainty, certain elements that define an exact trajectory for the future history of man. In virtue of what has already been seen, nothing, we may conclude, can prevent mankind in the future from

a. gradually becoming totalised upon itself.

b. developing 'from below' an automatism, in such a way as to release an increasing quantity of useful energy.

c. becoming spiritualised 'from the top', through the continually more advanced transformation of the energy released by technical progress.

3. The involuted structure of mankind

What I have just been saying about the physiology of the Noosphere takes on its full value only when it is completed by a consideration of its phylogenetic development. From this point of view, from the point of view, that is, of systematics, mankind appears as a fascicle of potential species continually forced, by planetary compression, to a state of mutual involution and continually enabled, by psychical interpenetration, to effect it. Zoologically speaking, we might say, the human group may be defined as the product of a constant ramification (speciation), constantly controlled and synthesised by convergence in a medium that is spatially and psychically curved. This allows us to posit the following two important laws:

a. The first, which we have already recognised, is that hominisation is essentially a process of collective unification.

b. The second, however, is more novel: it is that in this operation we must take into account the fact that men, not only individually but still more ethnically, represent complementary elements that differ qualitatively. As a result of its naturally ramified structure, mankind is made up of what one might call a large number of reflective 'isotopes'—each of which has its own particular virtues. Not to allow for this diversity in every human 'splinter', and so monitor their developments and ensure their correct proportions would be as dangerous as to try to counter the twofold force, external and internal, that obliges them to fold back upon themselves.

Let me insist again: the different structural properties I have just been enumerating are not sufficient to solve the problem now presented to man as a consequence of his evolution. They do, however, determine the general conditions of such a solution. So true is this, that any plan or project in which a single one of them is contradicted or overlooked can unhesitatingly —like a memorandum on squaring the circle—be thrown into the waste-paper basket.

Galluis, 3 August 1948

CHAPTER XVII

WHAT IS LIFE?

What is life?

Under the convergent influence of physics, chemistry, biology and the history of our planet, we are now beginning, I think, to see the outline emerging of an answer to that question: and it may readily, I believe also, be reduced to the three following propositions.

1. In a quite general way, we might say that life (defined by its principal attributes of assimilation, reproduction, heredity, and consciousness) is now seen by science not as a physico-chemical anomaly, but as the extreme form taken under certain conditions (a suitable temperature, a sufficiently long period of transformation etc.) by a *universal*, though generally disguised, *property* of the stuff of the cosmos. This amounts to saying that life can legitimately be regarded as having been continually present everywhere under pressure in the universe—coming to birth whenever and wherever it can—and, where it has once appeared, intensifying to its maximum in the immensities of Time and Space.

2. More precisely, life continually has a greater tendency to appear to us, scientifically, as a *specific effect of corpuscular complexity*, allied to the building up of very large and very complex particles. In spite of the existence of numerous critical thresholds, the curve that leads from large molecules to multicellular beings runs without any break in continuity: that being precisely the curve along which emerge (outside the play of chance and large numbers) the 'vital' effects of indeterminacy, self-arrangement, and consciousness.

3. That being granted, can we say that there is a relation between these two drifts?—between the mysterious drift of the world towards states of progressively greater complexity and interiority, and that other drift (much more fully studied and better charted) which draws the same world towards states of progressively greater simplicity and exteriority? And what is the relation? Quantitatively, one would say, the two movements (life and entropy) are decidedly unequal in importance; but are they not in reality of the same amplitude, the same order, and in some way complementary to one another? And, in that case, in what form can we foresee the phenomenon's final state of equilibrium? That last question may well be coming to sum up and express for the science of tomorrow, the essential riddle of the universe.

'Les Nouvelles Littéraires', 2 March 1950:
answer to an enquiry conducted by André George

CAN BIOLOGY, TAKEN TO ITS EXTREME LIMIT, ENABLE US TO EMERGE INTO THE TRANSCENDENT?

If biology is taken to its extreme limit in a certain direction, can it effect our emergence into the transcendent? To that question, I believe, we must answer that it can: and for the following reasons.

Although we too often forget this, what we call evolution develops only in virtue of a certain internal preference for survival (or, if you prefer to put it so, for self-survival) which in man takes on a markedly psychic appearance, in the form of a *zest for life*. Ultimately, it is that and that alone which underlies and supports the whole complex of all the bio-physical energies whose operation, acting experimentally, conditions anthropogenesis.

In view of that fact, what would happen if one day we should see that the universe is so hermetically closed in upon itself that there is no possible way of our emerging from it—either because we are forced indefinitely to go round and round inside it, or (which comes to the same thing) because we are doomed to a total death? Immediately and without further ado, I believe—just like miners who find that the gallery is blocked ahead of them—we would lose the heart to act, and man's impetus would be radically checked and 'deflated' for ever, by this fundamental discouragement and *loss of zest*.

That can mean only one thing: that by becoming reflective the evolutionary process *can continue only if it sees that it is irreversible, in other words transcendent*: since the complete irreversibility of a physical magnitude, in as much as it implies escape from the conditions productive of disintegration which are proper to time and space, is simply the biological expression of transcendence.

Evolution, the way out towards something that escapes total death, is the hand of God gathering us back to himself.

Probably written in May 1951, for the
'Semaine des Intellectuels catholiques'

CHAPTER XIX

RESEARCH, WORK AND WORSHIP[1]

'Go quietly ahead with your scientific work without getting involved in philosophy or theology . . .'
Throughout my whole life, that is the advice (and the warning) that authority will be found repeatedly to have given me.

And such, too, I imagine the directive given to many brilliant youngsters who are now, when the time is so opportune, entering the field of research.

Such, too, the attitude of which, with all respect and yet with the assurance I draw from fifty years spent living in the heart of the problem, I should like to remark to those it properly concerns that it is psychologically unviable and, what is more, directly opposed to the greater glory of God.

1. The scientific Spirit and faith in the Ahead

To understand what follows, it is necessary to bear in mind the organic and essential relationship that in every domain makes human work depend on a sufficiently powerful magnetic attraction exercised by the term of that work. If the climber is to conquer the peak (and the steeper the peak, the more this is true), he must have a passionate will to reach the top. That is a universal law. It must, therefore, apply in the case of science: this famous science whose conquests are extolled and used by everyone—but without ever asking them-

---

[1] The last paper sent by Père Teilhard before his death. It was written shortly after his last work, Le Christique (to be published later).

selves from what deep psychological source so irresistible and so general a human impulse draws its strength.

For a century now, scientific research has become both quantitatively (in the number of individuals engaged in it), and qualitatively (in the importance of the results obtained) a major—if not the principal—form of reflective activity on earth.

That means that there must be some extremely powerful motive force (and where can that be found?) to maintain and accelerate such a movement in our world today.

Let us see if we can find an answer to the question.

What initially makes man a 'scientist' (and this runs on from what is seen already in the higher animals) would appear to be the speculative attraction of *curiosity* combined with the economic stimulus of an *easier life*. To discover and invent for pleasure as well as from necessity—to improve the conditions in which one lives: this twofold need of diversion and comfort may rightly be regarded as the original impulse behind research.

At the same time we have to recognise that, accompanying the latest developments of knowledge, a new and much more powerful psychical stimulus is making itself felt in today's seeker: not simply the appetite for *well-being*, but the sacred and impassioned hope of attaining *fuller-being*.

Until very recent times, man had seemingly become resigned to the idea that the most he could do in this world was to continue to exist *as he is*, but in the best possible conditions.

Now, however, two new intellectual factors, working together, have brought a change. These two are:

a. first, the discovery that life was the result and the expression of an evolution.

b. secondly, the simultaneous discovery that scientific control of the motive forces of this evolution had made it possible for man to develop his own ultra-evolution.

Thus, a new prospect opens up, and our hearts entertain a new ambition: not simply to *survive* or *live well*, but to *super-live*, by forcing our way into some higher domain of consciousness and action.

Henceforth, no intellectual seeker worthy of the name can work or can continue to work unless, in the depths of his being, he is sustained by the idea of carrying further, and to its extreme limit, the progress of the world he lives in.

In other words, potentially at least, every seeker has today become by functional necessity, a 'believer in the Ahead', a man whose allegiance is to the 'ultra-human'.

Such, to my mind, is the present situation—and it involves practical consequences, as follows.

2. *The conflict between science and religion, and its solution*

What makes science appear dangerous in the eyes of religious authority is that it may well multiply 'objections' in the mind of those who embrace it, and develop a tendency to doubt.

In the light of what I have just been saying, the problem presents itself in a different way and at a deeper level.

What should, in fact, make superiors think twice before they send a young man to work in a laboratory (or a factory—it comes basically to the same thing) is not so much the fear that he may develop a 'spirit of criticism', as the certainty of exposing him to the fire of a new faith (faith in man), to which he is probably a stranger. '*Urere aut uri*'—'burn or be burned'.

The more religious-minded the person chosen for such work, the greater the odds that, in line with what he has been taught, he considers, religiously speaking, the advances and achievements of science simply as something inessential added to and subsidiary to the Kingdom of God.

And the more dedicated a scientist he is, on the other hand, the greater the chance that he will immediately be enamoured of a new outlook which attributes absolute value to the natural object of his most deep-rooted appetites.

In our days, circumstances are such that it is absolutely impossible for a Christian to dedicate himself sincerely to research (or in consequence to stand on an equal footing with his non-Christian colleagues) unless he shares the fundamental vision which animates that research: unless, that is, he first solves the basic contradiction that nine times out of ten will still be found in him, between the values of the traditional Above of the Gospel and those of the new human Ahead.

To tell a religious, therefore, to take up science, without at the same time allowing him, in so doing, to re-think his whole view of religion, is indeed, as I started by saying, to give him an impossible assignment—and to condemn him in advance to producing results of no real value, in an interior life that is torn two ways.

The situation is all the more 'crazy' in that to solve the dilemma in no way involves (I shall have spent my life emphasising this) a dilution of the Christian (and Ignatian) Spirit; it means so strengthening it that it reaches its highest expression.

This is not the place to develop once again my now familiar thesis, that Christ ultimately finds the plenitude of his creative action in a universe of the convergent type that science makes known to us, and in such a universe *alone*—in virtue of the existence, at last perceived, of a natural and supreme centre of cosmogenesis in which he can take up his dwelling.

On the other hand, there is something else which, I believe, I should emphasise more forcibly than ever: I mean the degree to which, simply by the fact of this transposition of the risen Christ to a higher pole of cosmic evolution, the Christian scientist is not only 'equi-animated' but 'super-animated', in comparison with the non-Christian scientist, in his enthusiasm for research. And the reason for this is that the former sees the ultra-human taking shape in the future not simply in the form of some vague collective but with the features of some Person who is supremely well defined and exerts a supreme magnetism.

Thus in the mind and heart of the Christian who has become 'an artisan of the earth', there is no trace of the conflict that some anticipate with dread: a splendid harmony is established between worship of the Above and faith in the Ahead.

And this, again, when he meets them on the very ground of allegiance to the world, gives him the proud privilege of saying to his humanist or Marxist fellow-worker, 'Plus et ego . . .'

3. A practical step to be considered: specialised religious training for scientific and industrial workers

We may well recognise that the God of the Above and the God of the Ahead are one and the same, but how are we to reconcile them?

For the last fifty years scientist-priests and worker-priests have been launched, in a haphazard way, into a sort of guerrilla warfare[2]; and they have been feeling very much what I have felt, and have been trying, more or less as I have, to solve the problem 'each for himself'.

Surely the time has come to sift, to codify, and systematically pass on to new recruits the results of this experience? In other words, before sending young men into the laboratories or factories should we not in future do more than select them in

[2] The worker-priest's 'social' demand for better-life obscures the neo-humanistic aspiration for, faith in, fuller-life. But to my mind, that faith is always present, and constitutes the chief and most vital part of the 'worker-spirit'. (Cf. the repeated evidence provided by Paul Vaillant-Couturier, Dr Rivet, and others.)

view of their qualifications and intellectual tastes? Should we not rather:

1. Examine them.
2. Train them, from the point of view of their spiritual aptitude to distinguish and seek after 'the Christic' in and through the 'ultra-human'?

This is a step, it is perfectly clear, that must be taken.

The natural and logical conclusion, it follows, that our minds must accept, is to envisage the establishment, in one form or another, of 'specialised seminaries'. In these (either in short periods of training or in longer stages) the young research students or workers of tomorrow would be introduced by carefully selected seniors to a theology that would be more concerned than it is now to make plain the genetic links between the Kingdom of God and human effort.

As a foundation, then, we need intellectual training: but spiritual education, I need hardly say, is equally important. This would take the form of the practice of the *Exercises*, rethought (exactly as in the case of dogma) along the lines of a clearer appreciation of the virtues, at once Christic and Christifying, to be found in man's works and activities.

'The Foundation', 'The Kingdom', 'The Two Standards'[3] ... since those essential meditations were conceived at a time when man was still regarded as inserted, fully formed, in a static universe, they do not (in their present form) make allowance for the legitimate attraction exerted upon us, from now on, by the Ahead. They do not accord to the progress of hominisation its full value of sanctifying and of producing communion. In consequence, they do not provide the seeker (or the worker) of today with what they most look for in their faith: that is, (as a Jociste[4] would say) the right to tell them-

[3] Meditations in the *Spiritual Exercises* of St Ignatius. (Ed.)
[4] A member of the *Jeunesse ouvrière chrétienne* (Young Christian Workers). (Tr.)

selves that they meet and consummate the Total Christ directly, *by working*.

It is not only dogmatic Christology, indeed, but the very notion of Christian perfection that has to be revised and over-hauled (in its orientation) as soon as it is transposed into a new universe (the universe, in fact, of the laboratory and the factory) in which the creature is not simply 'a tool to be used' but much more 'a co-element to be integrated' by mankind in genesis—a universe in which the old earth–heaven conflict vanishes (or is correctly adjusted) in the new formula, 'To heaven through fulfilment of earth.'

We need a new theology, then, and a new approach to perfection, which must gradually be worked out in our houses of study and retreat houses, in order to meet the new needs and aspirations of the 'workers' we live among.

But what we need perhaps even more (in as much as the researchers and workers of today are only the advance guard of our rising society) is for a new and higher form of worship to be gradually disclosed by Christian thought and prayer, adapted to the needs of all of tomorrow's believers without exception.

New York, March 1955

APPENDIX

It seemed appropriate to conclude by giving the reader the text of a letter (dated 2 November 1947) from Père Teilhard to E. Mounier, on the occasion of the Châtenay conference at which the latter presided. (Ed.)

My dear friend,

Since it is now clear that I cannot be present at your conference, I want at least to send you a few words which will tell you how much I shall be with you, and with all of you, in heart. I have not been able to find the time to write a paper for you; but I am anxious to draw your attention to the following point—almost self-evident, it is true—which I should have liked to put forward and discuss with your group.

When we speak of a 'theology of modern science', it obviously does not mean that by itself science can determine an image of God and a religion. But what it does mean, if I am not mistaken, is that, given a certain development of science, certain representations of God and certain forms of worship are ruled out, as *not being homogeneous* with the dimensions of the universe known to our experience. This notion of homogeneity is without doubt of central importance in intellectual, moral and mystical life. Even though the various stages of our interior life cannot be expressed strictly in terms of one another, on the other hand they must agree in scale, in nature and tonality. Otherwise it would be impossible to develop a true spiritual unity in ourselves—and that is perhaps the most legitimate, the most imperative and most definitive of the demands made by man of today and man of tomorrow.

If we accept that, we may, I think, go on to say that the most important modifications introduced by science into our perception and conception of the stuff of the world are as follows:

1. *The total organicity of the universe in time and space.* Every element in the world as we now see it, and every event (although limited, in its individualised trajectory, to a short historical segment) is in reality co-extensive (in its preparatory stages, in its inclusion in the general framework, and in its completion) *with the totality* of a Space-Time, from which it is impossible for our experience to emerge, either going backwards or ahead (except, in the latter direction, through death and ecstasis).

2. *The atomicity* of the universe. By that I mean the property possessed by the world (a property suspected since the time of the Greeks, but established—and with what fantastic realism —only for the last fifty years) of being elementarily made up of an incredible, utterly bewildering, multitude of elementary grains, progressively more numerous and smaller as we move further down—into the infinitesimal. And from this is derived, at the foundation of things, the vast and inevitable role of chance and tentative gropings.

3. As a consequence, *the primordial function of arrangement (or unification)*, consciousness appearing in an experientially evident alliance with a gradual complication of arrangement within corpuscular systems of an ever higher order.

It is within a real framework defined by these three main axial lines that an acceptable theology must henceforth be put forward. Metaphysics has over-emphasised an abstract, physically indeterminate idea of being. Science, for its part, uses certain exact 'parameters' to define for us the nature and requirements, in other words the physical stuff, of 'participated' being. It is these parameters that must in future be respected by every concept of Creation, Incarnation, Redemption and Salvation—as, indeed, of course by every 'demonstration' of the existence of God.

Make what use you please of these reflexions. But don't print them . . .'[1]

With renewed good wishes

ever yours

Teilhard

---

[1] Religious obedience prevented Père Teilhard from publishing any of his writings except for a number of scientific articles. (Ed.)

INDEX

Absolute, 41–2, 43, 70
action; amorisation of activity, 171;
and contemplation, 75; demand
for infallibility and irreversibility, 161–2, 163; philosophy of,
174–6, 177–8; value of Christian,
17, 17n, 68; zest for, 184. See effort
activance, 171n, 183, 184; conditions
of, 176–8, 180; principle of
maximum, 175; and the real,
174—5, 182
agnosticism, 104, 162
Ahead, 219; and Above, 202, 203,
217, 218; belief in, 215
amorisation, 171, 191
analysis, 24–8, 29, 50
anthropocentrism, 132
anthropogenesis, 154–5, 156, 157,
159, 162, 163, 165, 168, 212
atoms, 25, 47, 56, 91, 155
attachment, see detachment

Baianism, 116
baptism, 58
being; goodness, 39–40; fuller, 81;
new concept, 182; participated,
14, 180–1, 181n, 182n, 185, 185n,
222–3; primacy, 44; unity and
unification, 45, 186. See creative
union
biology, 35, 87, 90, 96, 212–13
biosphere, 61, 91, 93
Blériot, Louis, 204
Blondel, Maurice, 13n
body, human, 11–13, 35
Bossuet, J. B., 132
brain, 82, 155, 156, 159, 200
Buddha, 197

cells, 13, 25, 46, 91
centration, 163
Centre, 48, 51, 53, 56, 108, 122, 149,
163, 165, 180. See Christ, Omega
cephalisation, 155, 156, 167
cerebralisation, 153n, 156, 157, 158
chance, 94
charity, 34, 70, 123; universalised,
dynamic and synthesised, 167–71
Christ, 79, 110, 198; Alpha and
Omega, 34; body of, 11, 65;
centre of convergence, 35, 122;
consummation, 34, 166; cosmic
attributes, 189, 197; the evolver,
167, 169, 170; formative power,
72–3; head of creation, 167;
historical existence: significance,
62–3; humanity and super-
humanity, 164; identical with
Omega, 54, 58–9, 65, 67, 164–7;
Kingship, 19, 124, 165–6; power
to stimulate and satisfy, 109–10;
total, 68, 72, 220; universal, 14–
20, 55n, 59–66, 68, 71, 72, 75, 84,
122–4, 125, 127, 150, 169, 172. See
Christogenesis, Incarnation,
Omega
Christianity; and creative union,
53; dissatisfaction with, 120, 121,
125, 127; and evolution, 189–90;
and Humanism, 146–50; and
modern world, 118–19, 128; rejuvenation, 123–7; religion of
action and progress, 106–7, 108,
111–12, 124; and science, 21, 35–6,
187–91; and unbelief, 115–17
Christique, Le, 214n
Christogenesis, 168, 169, 189

Multiple—*continued*
m., 60–1; and evil, 79–80; and the
human soul, 47; and impulse towards unity, 66–7; and multiplication of living beings, 67n; the
One and the M., 16, 45, 74, 184;
reduction to, 50; unification by
Christ, 62, 76
mystical Body, 124, 185n
mystical Milieu, 74–7
mysticism; and science, 83;
Western, 106–7, 112

Neanderthaloids, 153
Neolithic age, 154
New Spirit, The, 151
Newton, Sir Isaac, 132
noosphere, 91, 93, 96, 173, 207, 208
nothingness, 46–7, 51
numbers, large, 90, 94, 95, 97

Omega, 48, 56, 63, 67, 207n; concentration of the Multiple in, 60;
culmination of anthropogenesis,
163; identical with Christ, 54, 56,
57, 164–5, 168, 170
original sin, 16, 80, 81, 126

pan-Christism, 58–9, 124
pantheism, 59, 116, 120, 124
Parousia, 84–5, 127
particles; elementary, 47; ultimate,
25–6, 27
Pascal, Blaise, 132; second infinite,
24
passivities, 71–3, 75
past, the, 78–80, 132–3
Paul, St, 74, 122, 181n; and Christ,
14, 18, 54–6, 57, 165, 189; and
Pleroma, 85
personalisation, 136–7, 160, 163
personalism, 137–41, 143, 147, 148–
149, 150

pessimism, 81, 126–7, 129–30, 131,
133
phenomenon of man, 132, 142, 156,
163; and communism, 140;
dimensions and significance, 93–
97; scientific approach, 87–92
Phenomenon of Man, The, 86n
philosophy; of action, 174, 176,
177–8; and notions of immobility
and substance, 182
physicalism, 55–6
physics, 35, 49, 87–8, 90, 93, 95, 99,
134; new, 96–7, 182
Pithecanthropus, 153
Pleroma, 59, 85, 181n
prayer, 70, 75
prehominians, 153–4
Prime Mover, problem of, 179–80
progress, 81, 134–7, 141, 190
psycho-dynamics, 172
purity, 34, 70

real, 174–5, 176, 186n
recurrence, law of, 46, 53. *See*
creative union
Redemption, 80, 190, 223
reflexion, 160, 195
religion, 98–100, 102, 103, 104; a
biological phenomenon, 100,
110–11; Buddhism, 106–7; of the
earth, 120, 148; Eastern religions,
105–6, 107; Islam, 104–5; and
science, 21, 35–6, 187–91; of the
universe, 113–14, 117. *See* Christianity
religious training, 218–20
Renaissance, 106, 113, 187
renunciation, 107
research, 22, 35, 83, 190, 215;
Jesuits' role, 201–2, 204–5; rise of,
199–201, 215; sacred character,
114–15
Resurrection, cosmic significance,
63–4